PLAYING WITH BEES

FREDERICK S. SOUTHWICK, M.D.

Southwick Press

2023
Southwick Press
Gainesville, Florida

ISBN 979-8-9887971-0-4

In Praise of
Playing With Bees

"I originally interviewed Fred Southwick for the Advanced Leadership Initiative (ALI) in 2009 and I have followed his admirable career since he completed that fellowship. Through his sometimes fraught journey, Fred has never lost sight of his North Star: improving the health and well-being of patients. He has become a well known and widely respected champion of better care throughout the nation. *Playing With Bees* documents his at times painful journey trying to apply many of the methods taught by the Institute of Healthcare Improvement (IHI) to improve the quality and safety of patient care.

Fred's courage, persistence, and willingness to tolerate multiple stings eventually led to major successes at the local level. Reading about his real-life examples and lived experiences will help both patients and those dedicated to improving patient care quality and safety navigate the at times treacherous terrain of the US healthcare system. He ends with a vision of the ideal health system that we should all aspire to achieve, and he creatively illuminates the 100-million-year-old honeybee system as the framework for the transformation of our healthcare system."

–Donald M., Berwick, MD MPP, President Emeritus and Senior Fellow, Institute for Healthcare Improvement, and former Administrator of the Centers for Medicare and Medicaid Services

"In this candidly personal, scientifically informed, and often deeply moving book, Dr. Fred Southwick sheds light on numerous problems plaguing health care in hospitals and prescribes a powerful solution: systems-sensitive leadership. Using the fascinating metaphor of bees and their cooperative hives, he shows that the difference in the quality of outcomes – sometimes life or death – lies in how well leaders empower others in a complex system to carry out their work in harmony. This is a powerful message that should resonate beyond health care to leaders in all sectors."

–Rosabeth Moss Kanter, Ph.D., Harvard Business School professor and author, most recently, of *Think Outside the Building: How Advanced Leaders Can Change the World One Smart Innovation at a Time*

"Fred Southwick describes how he went from laboratory physician to expert in health care safety. It all began when his wife almost died from a medical error. Later, Fred himself lost a limb after surgery. He then used his scientific skill to understand how medical errors happen and how they can be prevented. He discovered that health care safety requires a team where errors are few; actions are well designed and executed; and everyone is committed to excellence."

As Fred points out, this excellence is what bees have been doing for millions of years. And even humans can do it. As an example, aviation's safety record has been excellent over decades. Medicine needs to do the same. If you want to get started, read this book."

–Mark A. Kelley MD - pulmonary-critical care physician and educator at Massachusetts General Hospital and Harvard Medical School. Previously Professor and Vice Dean at Penn Health System in Philadelphia and an Executive and Vice President at Henry Ford Health System in Detroit.

In this remarkable book, Dr. Fred Southwick recounts lessons from a long career spent analyzing and addressing our problems with quality, safety and patient respect. Even more important he shows us that there are plenty of solutions, ranging from major systemic changes to specific practices at the frontlines on the wards. The biggest barrier is our inherent resistance to change, which thwarts political consensus and saps political will. Here too, Dr. Southwick provides important guidance on the way forward. Anyone interested in fighting for an effective, affordable, safe, and just health care system should read this book.

--Vikas Saini, M.D. President, Lown Institute

"Thanks for sharing this great book! The practical and effective ways to lead and to build teamwork are critical for us all today. In this time of complex care, leading in this new way will lead us to better outcomes and improved patient journeys.

This book also shows the power of working on CQ (curiosity quotient). In this way, we learn about what matters most to our patients, their care teams, and our staff, all vital parts of leading in these complex times."

–Maureen Bisognano, MS, President and CEO 2010-2015, Executive Vice President, and COO 1995-2010 Institute of Healthcare Improvement (IHI)

"Each day, countless people trade what they're wearing for scrubs. Those who exercise this re-robing ritual do so expecting that their talents, training, and best intentions will add appreciated value into the lives of others, and into their own lives as well. Sometimes, these promises are kept, oftentimes with dazzling effect. However, that is not always true, sometimes disappointingly, occasionally tragically.

Fred Southwick's fantastic contributions, continuing with *Playing with Bees*, are in explaining why best, even heroic, individual efforts by healthcare professionals are compromised, and in detailing what can be done to close the gap, so that lived reality is closer to the best of promises and expectations.

The bee community metaphor is perfect in highlighting the system nature of the problem and of its solution. Healthcare does depend on individual excellence, even genius, but, fundamentally, success is a "systems effect". It depends on effective collaboration, so many individual efforts integrate harmoniously through collective action towards common purpose.

Bravo to Dr. Southwick for a lifetime of commitment to his individual patients and even more so for his devotion to fostering systems of care by which he and his colleagues have far greater chance of being successfully in doing truly great things for us and those we love.

–Steve Spear, DBA MS MS MIT
Sloan School of Management, Senior Lecturer
Institute for Healthcare Improvement, Senior Fellow
See to Solve, Founder Author, *The High Velocity Edge* and *Wiring the Winning*

"I enjoyed reading *Playing with Bees*. The combination of personal stories and theoretical models work well together. Dr. Southwick is to be commended for his patience and tolerance in advocating for new approaches to improve the quality of patient care."

–Richard Pettingill – President and CEO of Allina Hospitals and Clinics 2002-2009

Table of Contents

Dedication

I dedicate this book to my brother Steve, my cheerleader and friend throughout my life. He lost his battle with prostate cancer; however, his generous spirit and kindness live on in our hearts.

I also dedicate this book to my beautiful wife Kathie, who has patiently supported me through health challenges and the ups and downs of my career. She continues to be my source of strength.

Acknowledgments

First and foremost, I want to thank my sister Marcia Southwick, a former professor of creative writing, gifted poet, and graduate of the Iowa Writers' Workshop. Without her mentorship and continual encouragement, this book would never have been written.

I also want to thank Dr. Nila Radhakrishnan, who is the most effective adaptive leader I have known. Her enthusiasm and support for improving the quality and safety of patient care have been inspirational. I also want to thank the Hospital Medicine faculty who have worked with me as team members. When the going got tough, their kind words and respect were uplifting, and their embrace of quality improvement and the application of plan-do-study-adjust cycles transformed our division into a leading force for change.

Thank you to Dr. Mark Kelley, who devoted hours to our discussions, and together we constructed the final chapter and the back cover. Also thank you to Richard Pettingill and Don Davis, who provided many helpful suggestions for improvement.

Finally, I want to thank Professor Rosabeth Moss Kanter who headed the Harvard Business School Advanced Leadership Initiative Fellowship Program and reminded her students repeatedly that bringing about meaningful change is "like dancing backward in high heels."

Preface

Honey doesn't lose its sweetness because it is made by bees that sting.
—Matshona Dhliwayo

My face was flushed by the warm air of the Nebraska summer as I rushed out the back door of my Grandmother Gangi's kitchen. The screen door squeaked and sprung back with a loud *slam* as I ran into the backyard and towards the large honeysuckle vines. I was four years old, and this is one of my most prominent early memories.

I subsequently learned that I was a handful as a toddler, in constant motion and always on a mission. Only the month before, for example, I had discovered my parents' intriguing set of wedding plates. As I examined the milky white and silver pattern, several dishes fell to the floor with a loud *crash*.

My mission that morning, however, was to play with bees. I was fascinated by honeybees. I loved their dark stripes and yellow-brown color and the hum of their wings as they gingerly approached the honeysuckle flowers and gathered nectar. I was in awe of their ability to quickly change direction as they moved from flower to flower. Their sheer number was fascinating, and they all looked so busy. Each seemed to understand their role in a carefully choreographed dance.

My curiosity drove me to observe them more closely, and – as a tactile boy – I instinctively reached out to touch them. I was quickly greeted with a sharp sting. I winced and whimpered in pain, and my chubby little finger quickly turned red and began to swell. But the pain rapidly subsided as my intense fascination returned, and I went back to watching the bees move from flower to flower.

I was determined to try again to capture a bee, and once more I was stung. No longer surprised, I continued reaching out to grab the bees. A little sting would not dissuade me, and eight stings later, I captured a bee. Once the bee had released its stinger it could no longer hurt me, and the bee stayed perched on my palm allowing close observation of its striking coloring, slender legs, and delicate wings. As my brain captured these exciting images, a broad smile spread across my face. The rewards of my quest far exceeded the minor pain of a few bee stings.

Satisfied with my adventure, I returned to the kitchen door and Gangi quickly responded to my banging and opened the door. With an expression of dismay, she noticed the red welts on my right hand, as well as one on my cheek. She asked in her sweet, high-pitched, melodious voice, "Freddie, dear, what happened?" With an excited and happy expression, I exclaimed, "The bees, Gangi, the bees!"

"Well, Freddie, you must be more careful. Bees can hurt you."

The next day, I returned to the honeysuckle vines and tried moving my hand toward one of the bees very slowly. I then decided to hold my hand still and, within a minute, a bee landed. I observed the bee's every move. I learned that if I didn't threaten the bees they wouldn't sting. I watched the bee clean his head with his front feet. I was transfixed by these little creatures. So disciplined, and so steady in their work. No stings that day. When I returned to the kitchen, Gangi was pleased when she saw I had no new welts.

I now realize that my childhood experiences playing with bees revealed the same behavior traits that attracted me to the field of patient care, quality, and safety. Thanks to my mother's encouragement and patience (including tolerating a few broken dishes), I have always been curious and remain single-minded in the pursuit of my goals. Just as I returned to the honeysuckle vines despite multiple bee stings, I have repeatedly returned to my quality improvement projects despite . . . well, let's call it 'resistance'.

Playing with Bees recounts my journey trying to improve the quality and safety of patient care. My hope is that other healthcare professionals as well as the lay public can learn from my mistakes and successes. Just as I discovered how to examine honeybees without being stung, I will describe how I have accomplished similar successes in the field of medical quality and safety.

This book presents my personal, heart-rending experiences as both a patient and a doctor that were pivotal in motivating me to improve the quality and safety of patient care. I then present encounters with the challenges that patients and their families have faced in trying to overcome disabilities caused by medical errors, and their efforts to recover.

I next describe how healthcare professionals must aspire to create systems of care that, in many ways, reflect the example of the honeybee hive. To illustrate the challenges associated with changing our systems of care I share both my failures and successes as an adaptive leader, the lessons I have learned, and the best practices for achieving the behavioral changes required to establish highly reliable health systems. The need for robust health systems is even more apparent following the pandemic and I am confident that these lessons can be applied to transforming any system, even those resistant to change.

Who should read this book? Anyone who is fed up with the failures and frustrations of healthcare systems and the preventable errors that continue to cause millions of permanent injuries and over 250,000 deaths in the US annually. More specifically, administrators, physicians, nurses, health profession students, patients, and their families. In fact, I recommend this book to anyone who requires health care and is concerned about our error-prone healthcare delivery systems.

My hope is that *Playing with Bees* will empower and encourage others to find new solutions. I am optimistic that administrators, healthcare professionals and patients can come together to transform our healthcare systems into systems comparable to the coordination and efficiency of honeybees.

Frederick Southwick, MD

Chapter 1: Who Was Caring for Mary?

As long as medicine is an art, its chief and characteristic instrument must be human faculty. We come therefore to the very practical question of what aspects of human faculty it is necessary for the good doctor to cultivate... The first to be named must always be the power of attention, of giving one's whole mind to the patient without the interposition of oneself. It sounds simple but only the very greatest doctors ever fully attain it.
    —Dr. Wilfred Trotter

The secret of the care of the patient is in caring for the patient.
    —Dr. Francis Peabody

In 1988 I was an Assistant Professor at an Ivy League medical school, and my wife Mary was 33 years old and the mother of our two children Ashley, age 5, and Peter, age 8. She was healthy and physically active as a part-time dance instructor.

Mary's Story

Early one morning in November, Mary suddenly awoke complaining of sharp lightning-like pain in her right foot. The pain was so severe she could not tolerate the sheet touching her skin. Tears were streaming down her face as she writhed in pain.

This was the most intense pain I had ever witnessed as a physician. What was causing it?

Two weeks earlier, she and both of our children had had strep throat and were treated with amoxicillin. When her foot pain began, I suggested she stop her amoxicillin, which she did. However, unbeknownst to me, two days later she started taking the medication again.

My first step was to call our next-door neighbor, an orthopedic surgeon. He arrived at 6 a.m. and carefully examined her leg and foot and discovered that the muscles supplied by these nerves were weak. Could she have suffered a nerve injury instructing yesterday's dance class? Why would the onset of her pain be delayed by 16 hours? My neighbor prescribed Mary a strong pain medication, but the pain persisted, and she tossed, turned, and moaned the subsequent nights.

Next, we sought the advice of a renowned academic neurologist who specialized in peripheral nerve injuries. His tests were inconclusive, yet he predicted that it would take a year for the nerve to heal. Discouraged, we never heard from or saw him again. As a fellow faculty member, I was disheartened and angered by his callous responses.

Mary then developed blisters and her right ankle began to swell. A trusted internist agreed to see her in her clinic and made the diagnosis of thrombophlebitis (blood clots in the veins of her right leg) and recommended hospital admission. She was not on call that day and had family responsibilities to attend to, so she referred us to the Emergency Room for admission.

My heart sank and I felt we had been abandoned again.

Blood tests in the Emergency Room revealed an extremely high eosinophil count (7,000/μL, normal being < 350/μL), which usually indicates a severe allergic reaction. All previous medications, including amoxicillin, were discontinued. I was worried about Mary's unusual presentation and the relentless progression of the signs and symptoms. Unfortunately, the admitting intern was starting his first day in internal medicine and had only previously served on the surgical services.

Respectfully acknowledging the intern's inexperience, I attempted to assist him by pointing out the blisters on her hand and sole and asked if they might be biopsied. He thanked me for my suggestion, but never consulted a dermatologist or biopsied any of her lesions. "Why wouldn't they listen to my suggestion?" I wondered. But my role was to be the supportive husband and I needed to take off my doctor's coat.

On the fifth day of hospitalization, she suddenly grimaced in midsentence and complained, "Fred, I feel short of breath and my chest hurts when I take a deep breath." She was experiencing the complication we had been trying to prevent, pulmonary embolism.

"Does Mary need an umbrella?" I asked the consulting pulmonologist. (This is a wire mesh device that is inserted in a vein to prevent further clots from migrating to the lungs.) "No," I was told, "she doesn't need an umbrella. Her heparin doses were too low, and she has been subtherapeutic. I am really sorry about this. I can't tell you how many times these general internists screw up the heparin dosing."

I rushed to the senior physician's office. "Why was Mary not receiving adequate heparin doses?"

By his expression and comments, it was clear he was unaware of the mistake with her heparin dosage. He said I was welcome to speak to the resident. "Why don't you help him with her care?" he suggested. Being an academic physician myself I understood the pressures he was under, but this was my wife and the mother of my two children! I became frightened; who was in charge?

Two days later, Mary began complaining of a new type of chest pain, and her electrocardiogram (ECG) and cardiac enzyme blood tests revealed a myocardial infarction – a heart attack! I couldn't believe it - from an unexplained nerve injury to blood clots in her legs, to a massive blood clot in her lungs, and now, a heart attack.

Frustrated by the lack of supervision by the internal medicine attending, I transferred her care to a trusted cardiologist and Mary was placed in the Intensive Care Unit (ICU). Overnight, her lungs filled with fluid and her arterial oxygen levels became dangerously low. Fluid in her lungs was preventing sufficient oxygen delivery to her arteries. I recognized that Mary had developed acute respiratory distress syndrome (ARDS) and was now at high risk of dying.

The next morning, exhausted and breathless, Mary whispered to me, "I am so tired. I can't last much longer." I showed her a photo of our children and said, "But Mary, remember, you have to help raise Ashley and Peter. We love you and need you so much. You can't give up."

She nodded. We looked into each other's eyes as the anesthesiologist gave her a sedative and placed the breathing tube. I realized this might be our last communication in this world.

Peter and Ashley

As I sat in the waiting room, I felt like I was sitting on the gallows and that the hangman would arrive at any minute. I began thinking of all the wonderful things Mary had done for me. Mary loved to tell funny stories and was always the life of the party. I imagined that she was thinking of a joke at that very moment. That was Mary; she always looked at the humorous side of life. I thanked Mary's mother for raising such a wonderful person. I realized I should be thankful for the ten precious years we had had together.

That day, an expert pulmonologist-intensivist who had just returned from a trip rushed from the airport to Mary's bedside. He adjusted her ventilator settings and began administering vasopressors (agents to increase her blood pressure) because she had now developed shock. Her kidneys had stopped producing urine and a nephrologist was called to place a special hemofiltration apparatus designed to draw off fluid in the hopes of improving her lung function.

As the nephrologist manipulated the catheter, Mary's heart suddenly stopped pumping. All electrical activity in her heart ceased. Her heart monitor showed a flat line in place of the normal sharp upward R-wave of a heart in normal sinus rhythm. Such an asystolic cardiac arrest usually portends imminent death. As the alarms sounded, physicians and nurses from all over the hospital rushed to her bedside.

I bowed my head in prayer and squeezed the small wooden cross my brother had given me. My hands were sweating and my knuckles blanched as I tightly squeezed this small symbolic object. As hard as humanly possible, I thought, "Please, Mary, don't leave me. We need you so much. Don't give up."

Her heart began beating again. "Normal sinus rhythm," someone called out. She soon had a second asystolic arrest and was again brought back to normal sinus rhythm.

An hour after her two cardiac arrests, Mary's urine output suddenly increased, and her lung function rapidly improved as the fluid drained from her lungs. I knew she would survive.

As doctors say, she had 'turned the corner'. Within five days she was taken off the respirator and the endotracheal tube was removed. I rushed to Mary's bedside and gave her a kiss on the forehead. In a humorous tone, her first words to me were, "Hey, why are you here? You make me nervous!"

Peter and Ashley were able to grow up with the nurturing care of their loving mother. They are both now married and have children of their own. Mary and I did not beat the statistics when it came to staying together, yet we are both happily remarried, and life has moved on. However, the memories of Mary's frightening illness will be with us forever.

Little did I know that twenty years later, as a Director of Patient Care Quality and Safety, I would be engaged in applying the scientific method repeatedly to identify and correct defective processes within our health system.

Lessons from Science

In retrospect, my conclusion is that the physicians caring for Mary in the early part of her illness had not applied the scientific method to arrive at a timely diagnosis. I had been required to continually apply this method during my research training in infectious diseases at Massachusetts General Hospital. The first step is to ask, "Why?" and then to create a hypothesis that explains the outcome or manifestation observed. Experiments are then designed to test each hypothesis, measure their outcomes, and decide whether the hypothesis is correct.

If experimental results are negative, this indicates that the null hypothesis is correct, and that the original hypothesis is wrong. When this happened, I would be forced to go back to the drawing board, and with the help of other members of our laboratory, generate a new hypothesis or explanation and corresponding new series of experiments.

Using this approach, Mary's inpatient internist should have gone back to the drawing board at the time of hospital admission and at subsequent stages of her hospital course. He first should have asked why she had a nerve injury, blisters on her foot and hand, and eosinophilia. The neurologist's original hypothesis – that her nerve damage was due to a physical injury – could not explain her normal MRI, the blisters or her eosinophilia. In the later stages of her illness, it also could not explain her heart attack or respiratory failure. The involvement of multiple parts of the body should have suggested a systemic disorder rather than a local injury.

Later in her hospital course our cardiologist did reexamine all the manifestations of her disease and raised the possibility of systemic vasculitis (inflammation of the blood vessels). Damage to her coronary artery blood vessels would be expected to reduce the oxygen supply to the heart and explain her heart attack. Damage to the vessels in the lung could cause fluid to leak from the vessels into the lung and block oxygen exchange, explaining her ARDS and her low arterial oxygen levels. Damage to vessels in the kidneys could explain her inability to produce urine.

To test his hypothesis the cardiologist treated the possible vasculitis by administering high-dose corticosteroids and her rapid recovery fulfilled his hypothesis. Indeed, just prior to her discharge, an experienced immunologist confirmed that Mary had suffered a severe penicillin allergy that had caused her eosinophilia and vasculitis.

After Mary's Experience

At the time, I had thought Mary's hospital course was a one-in-a-million event. Little did I realize that Mary's case represented the tip of an iceberg. For us, however, the dust settled, and life returned to normal. But I kept asking myself, "How could my wife end up in the medical intensive care unit with less than a 10% chance of survival? Why did this happen and what have I learned from our near-death experience?"

The first and most powerful emotion I experienced was anger. I felt that the physicians we encountered in the initial phases of her illness were distracted, and that their actions implied that Mary's illness was of secondary importance next to their family obligations and research priorities.

Two years after Mary's illness I wrote an opinion piece in the *Annals of Internal Medicine* entitled "Who Was Caring for Mary?" (1) This piece called upon Academic Medical Centers to focus on patient care as their top priority and to reward and recognize clinical excellence. I challenged faculty to take ownership of patient management and supervise their residents more closely. Finally, the article stressed the importance of preventing the fragmentation of care by training internal medicine generalists who could skillfully integrate data from various specialties.

The reactions to my article were profound. The university health system called a special meeting after Mary's case was published and rededicated their medical center to clinical excellence. They also appointed a Chief Patient Care Quality Officer. Today they are among the leading medical centers when it comes to safe and high-quality patient care. In 2022, they received an "A" rating for patient safety by the independent national watchdog organization Leapfrog.

I received over 90 letters from physicians, many emphasizing the importance of communicating with patients. I was also invited to present at grand rounds conferences throughout the country, recounting the case and underscoring the importance of individual physician accountability and of rewarding clinical excellence in our medical centers. This message was well received. In fact, for the next decade, many academic medical center programs handed out the article "Who was Caring for Mary?" to all incoming residents.

The Beehive as a Guide to Systems Improvement

But was simply trying harder, taking responsibility, and focusing on each individual patient the whole solution? Many systemic conditions interfered with Mary's care.

Until 2007 I was not a systems thinker, and I had not yet considered how the honeybee hive system could be applied to health care. In this system, for instance, every worker bee fulfills their designated roles flawlessly and their efforts are seamlessly coordinated thanks to continual communication. Continual improvements in efficiency come from the bees serving as foragers and scouts and not from some distant higher authority. Decisions are made on the front lines by consensus. When it came to Mary's care – with the exception of her care in the ICU – these conditions were glaringly absent.

Let's consider this system more closely, as it provides important lessons for healthcare professionals.

To maximize survival, the honeybee system has evolved over 100 million years into one of the most efficient and carefully coordinated systems in the insect world. (2-4) The beehive system is designed to gather sufficient nectar and pollen to supply the caloric needs of bees for foraging, reproduction, and generation of heat during the cold winter months. Without sufficient honey, the bee colony will die over the winter. Honeybee behavior is predominantly genetically predetermined to assure the effective coordination of all the members of the beehive.

Human beings, on the other hand – particularly physicians – take pride in their individuality and creativity, but when excessive these conditions can limit the ability to work well in teams. They can therefore benefit from adaptive leaders; leaders who are adept at encouraging healthcare professionals to change how they practice medicine. Such individuals help to create cultural cues that encourage the teamwork required to create effective, efficient, highly coordinated, and safe healthcare delivery systems.

Finally, for a system to be effective everyone must share the same values and aspire to the same goals. For honeybees, as mentioned above, their unified mission is to generate sufficient honey to survive the cold winter.

In my Boston-based training programs, everyone's primary focus was on the care of the patient. We were taught that caring for patients was a sacred trust that we must always keep as our top priority whenever we were on call in the hospital. Our job was to collect all key historical facts, laboratory, and imaging findings and present them in a carefully organized format that would allow the hospital ward team to create an effective and efficient treatment plan to improve the health and well-being of our patients. This was our 'honey'.

On the contrary, the physicians who were caring for Mary appeared to regard research and family, rather than patient care, as their honey. I thought, "Shouldn't all healthcare professionals be aligned to aspire to the same honey – to provide uncompromising, efficient, effective, and safe patient care?"

Chapter 2: A Painful and Life-Altering Medical Error

Do not judge me by my success, judge me by how many times I fell down and got back up again.
—Nelson Mandela

Initially, I regarded Mary's near death due to medical errors as an exceedingly rare event. However, my own encounter with a serious medical error 24 years later served as another stark personal warning that our healthcare delivery systems continue to be error-prone. This reinforced my belief that our health systems should aspire to emulate honeybees.

My Story

I was excited to be at the beach on July 4, 2012. I had just completed a long and stressful rotation as an infectious diseases consultant. The roar of the surf has always calmed me down and I couldn't wait to get out in the water.

I woke early the next morning to find the ocean resembled a calm lake. There would be no surfing today. So I decided to get some exercise by paddling three miles and back along the shore on my stand-up paddle board. During the second mile, I noticed that my left calf began to feel tight and seemed to be cramping. I shifted my weight to my right leg, but the left calf cramping continued. I stopped paddling and sat down on the board, dangling my feet in the water. My cramp had resolved. I stood up and began paddling again. Within five minutes it started cramping again. The pain was surprisingly sharp.

I had had no recent injury to that leg, so why did my calf keep cramping?

Later, as my wife Kathie and I headed for breakfast, the left calf cramping resumed. I drank a large glass of orange juice in the hope that the cramp was due to low potassium levels, but the juice made no difference. Over the next six weeks, every time I walked any distance the cramp recurred. I subsequently began to experience calf and foot pain at night. When my foot finally turned white, I knew my symptoms were the result of reduced blood flow to the left calf and foot.

The injection of contrast dye to visualize my left leg arteries on an X-ray revealed the absence of all blood flow below my left knee. I underwent vascular surgery to explore my leg several times but no patent (open) vessels below my knee could be found, making arterial bypass surgery impossible. The only solution was an amputation.

I had hoped for a below-knee amputation to allow me to row and bicycle; however, this procedure failed, and within two weeks an above-the-knee amputation was performed. The loss was devastating. I began asking myself, "Who am I? An invalid?" Would I return to work? Could I participate in sports? Athletics had always been central to my identity, and I had participated in sports my entire life.

The next two weeks were spent sitting on the couch with my younger brother Steve. As we finished all five seasons of the series *Prison Break* on Netflix, I thought to myself, should I spend the remainder of my life watching television? With continued help and encouragement from my wife and my brother, I recovered. The journey was long, with many setbacks and successes (Figure 2-1). Pain in my residual limb was a continuous companion but could be reduced using an ice pack.

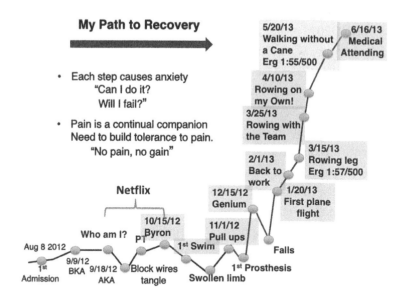

Figure 2-1. Timeline of my recovery from amputation
Shaded squares = improvements, Erg = rowing machine with time to complete 500 m.

An outstanding personal trainer named Byron assisted me in rebuilding my strength and regaining the 25 lbs. of muscle lost during my surgeries and early recovery. Other successes, high-lighted in the shaded boxes in Figure 2-1, included:

- My first swim
- Performing pull-ups
- Being fitted with my computer chip-controlled prosthetic leg, the Genium
- Taking my first plane flight to visit my parents
- Returning to work
- The creation of an innovative hinge leg by my prosthetist that allowed me to row on the Erg (a rowing machine) and achieve 500-meter times of under two minutes
- Rowing with members of the rowing team in a four-man boat
- Rowing on my own in my single rowing shell

Thanks to the coaching of a very experienced physical therapist, by May of 2013 – less than a year after the loss of my leg – I had learned how to walk without a significant limp.

I also experienced setbacks including overdoing a swimming exercise, leading to a badly swollen residual limb and a delay in fitting a prosthesis; receiving my first prosthesis – a heavy hydraulic leg that made walking very difficult; and my early falls while walking with my Genium prosthetic. These falls were soon eliminated by the proper adjustments.

Ultimately, in August of 2013, I returned to competitive rowing and competed in multiple races, thanks to the creativity of my prosthetist and the strong support of my rowing team. The coordinated efforts of the healthcare professionals and my family and friends were very much like worker bees, with a shared idea of honey: returning me to an active life.

My daily routines are now very different from my life before amputation, but by June 2013 I returned as the medical attending physician on the teaching service and resumed my efforts to improve the quality and safety of patient care. Although my pace was slower, I am able to manage physically and once again enjoy caring for patients, as well as supervising and teaching our residents and medical students. My trainees were very patient with me as we slowly moved from room to room, but thanks to the standardized rounding system I developed (see chapter 5), we completed rounds each day in less than two hours.

Lessons Learned

During one workout, I wondered aloud how this could have happened. The scientific method generated a hypothesis: "I have no systemic disorder or condition that can explain the absence of circulation in my left leg. There must have been physical damage to my left leg." Next, I asked, "What happened to my left leg that didn't happen to my right leg?"

There was only one difference in how the two legs had been

treated. In 1995, I suffered a torn left Achilles tendon and had to undergo surgical repair. After that surgery, whenever I waded into cool water my left foot turned blue while my right foot remained pink.

In early February of 2013, I requested the operative report from our medical records department. As I read the report from March 1995, I was surprised to find mention of a tourniquet, a belt used to restrict or stop bleeding. My surgery had taken over two hours (an average Achilles takes 15 minutes); should a tourniquet have been left on at very high pressure for such a lengthy surgery? Further, a ruptured tendon was noted, with extensive injury: "The collagen bundles were disrupted, creating a 'mop end' appearance to both the proximal and distal parts of the tendon." The reattachment of the tendon fragments had required extensive physical manipulation. Subsequent specimens from my amputated leg revealed that, at the time of amputation, the two arteries below my left knee had been destroyed.

In retrospect, the blue toes on my left foot following the tendon repair surgery reflected a traumatic injury and occlusion of two out of the three arteries supplying my left lower leg. For 17 years I had been functioning with a single patent artery in that leg. In simple terms: I realized I had lost my leg to a medical error.

Having dedicated the remainder of my career to preventing medical errors, I was suffering the consequences of the very problems I was trying to solve.

Upsetting the Bees

One of the tenets of patient safety is transparency, so I needed to share my experience with the world. If this could happen to a physician dedicated to improving the quality and safety of patient care, it could happen to anyone. On February 13, 2013, the *New York Times* Op-Ed section published, 'I Lost My Leg to a Medical Error'. (5)

Within hours Drs. Don Berwick and Lucian Leape, two of the founders of the patient safety movement, emailed thanking me for highlighting the urgency of preventing harm due to medical errors. The online comments from several orthopedic surgeons were scathingly negative. However, other doctors and many patients who had experienced similar injuries reached out describing their losses and thanked me for sharing my story.

Unexpectedly, I was also contacted by the hospital administration. They claimed that the editorial drew unfounded conclusions. How dare I accuse the orthopedic surgeon of making an error! In fact, my editorial had not blamed any single individual but instead highlighted the importance of teamwork and integrated systems for preventing future medical errors. The surgeon himself was irate, and he and the leadership in my health system misinterpreted my motives and purpose.

My story was quickly forgotten in the media, but the negative personal consequences of my actions proved to be long-lasting. I had misread the prevailing culture of our healthcare center and had moved too quickly, needlessly 'upsetting the bees' – bees from a different beehive. I had inadvertently set off a fight-or-flight reaction and, as well as resistance to dialogue and change. I experienced multiple stings (see chapter 7).

Absence of a Culture of Safety

Ideally, all health systems foster a culture of safety where those working within the system are empowered to speak out about medical errors. Sharing conditions on the front lines is critical for improving quality and safety. (6) For example, in our metaphor, imagine if worker bees who shared the locations of areas rich in nectar-carrying flowers were punished. The worker bees would hesitate to share locations, nectar harvesting would decrease and there would be insufficient honey to survive the winter. Similarly, punishing those who speak up about medical errors can stifle quality improvement.

But this was not about to stop me. I planned to continue to play with the bees, but I needed to become more strategic.

Chapter 3: Becoming a Patient Advocate

Listen to your patient. He's telling you the diagnosis.
—William Osler, MD

Despite the negative reactions discussed in the previous chapter, my editorial in the *New York Times* did pay one very positive dividend: many patients who had been harmed by medical errors shared their stories of being mistreated and having their emails and phone calls ignored. After hearing so many examples of medical harm, I created a blog entitled *Recovering from a Medical Error*. The goal was to encourage patients and families to publicly share their frustration with their medical treatment and, based on their experience, to provide suggestions for improvement.

Airing grievances is often the first step in the recovery process, and I also hoped that my blog would encourage readers to actively campaign for change. Over the first six months of processing and sharing my experiences with the world, I collected many other poignant stories of suffering and loss. As you will read below, a wide variety of medical errors can lead to devastating losses of function, health, and life.

Missed Diagnosis

One story was the saddest of all. A beautiful and vivacious 17-year-old high school student was looking forward to her prom. However beginning at age twelve she had experienced sudden fainting spells, usually in response to being startled. Sometimes when her cats unexpectedly jumped on her bed, or after her mom ran a blender early in the morning. Her spells began with feeling dizzy, and she would then turn blue and stop breathing. These frightening events required emergency ambulance transport to the hospital. The whole family was continuously on edge. They never knew when the next episode was coming.

At a large Canadian children's hospital, the neurologists initially diagnosed her with epilepsy. However, a year later this diagnosis was excluded. The doctors had no explanation for her continued fainting episodes. Then, while the family was on vacation, a severe spell left her weak and confused. Unable to walk, her parents had to take her home in a wheelchair. Continued workups at the same children's hospital yielded no explanations.

Then, when she was in the tenth grade, her grandmother read an article about Long QT Syndrome (LQTS). This is an inherited electrical conduction abnormality of the heart that can mimic epilepsy and even lead to sudden death. In individuals with LQTS, defibrillator placement prevents syncope and is usually lifesaving. The family was excited, feeling that they had a likely explanation for the spells. Her mother presented their discovery to the physician, who responded that it couldn't possibly be LQTS. She showed him an electrocardiogram (ECG) obtained at a smaller hospital near their home that showed a long QT interval, and she was told the interpretation was wrong.

Frustrated, the patient's mother switched neurologists in the hopes of a fresh perspective and asked him to consult a cardiologist. On consulting with a new cardiologist, he proved to be dismissive and condescending, and after an extensive work up, claimed there were no cardiac abnormalities. Meeting with their neurologist again, he had no further explanations, suggesting that she "go home and learn how to breathe through a spell," and that they were "wasting money on an ambulance." What was the family supposed to do?

Ten months later, this young girl died. Her graduation photo was supposed to be in the high school yearbook, not in an obituary. She was supposed to be going to the prom in a limo not being transported to her funeral in a hearse. There would be no high school graduation, no prom, and no time for goodbyes.

Genetic analysis subsequently revealed that the patient possessed the gene for LQTS, as did her father, who had received an implanted defibrillator. Further investigation revealed that her Holter monitor study (a 24-hour ECG) had not been fully analyzed. Episodes of prolonged QT and arrhythmia were discovered only after the patient's death, resulting in a successful malpractice suit.

Delay in Diagnosis

The story of a master carpenter and his wife also touched my heart. For years he had molded wood into the most magnificent heirloom furniture imaginable. He had a thriving architectural woodworking business and was always in demand, while his wife worked as a fundraiser and health policy advocate.

In 2001, at 50 years old, the patient had blood in his stool. A polyp (a potentially precancerous growth) was found in his colon and removed, but not completely. He was told the polyp had cancer cells, but at no time in the following seven years was he scheduled for a follow-up colonoscopy.

In 2005, after informing his primary care physician (PCP) that he had noticed blood, he was told it was caused by hemorrhoids, and felt it was "not his place to question or quibble" with this diagnosis. In mid-2007 he called the physician's office about blood in his stool and again was told it was just his hemorrhoids. In July 2008 he was diagnosed with a malignant neoplasm of the rectum, stage IV cancer, meaning the cancer had already metastasized to another organ or tissue.

After extensive surgery, high-dose chemotherapy that resulted in the loss of sensation in his hands and feet, as well as extensive radiotherapy and 14 months of changing wound dressings, he recovered and is now cancer-free. Sadly, the loss of sensation in his hands caused by the chemotherapy ended his career as a furniture maker. However, he describes that he recalled the words of Bob Dylan's song 'The Times They Are A-Changin: Shake your windows. And rattle your walls".

And that is exactly what he did.

He met with the chancellor of the medical center in the hopes of preventing similar events from happening to others. Immediately, the administration and physicians circled the wagons. As of writing, they have not yet apologized and continue to claim that the illness was a complication that could not have been prevented. However, the patient won his malpractice suit.

End-of-Life Care

Another poignant story about cancer treatment was shared by a passionate pharmacist and nationally renowned patient safety advocate. Her story:

> My dad had noticed that he lost his appetite and couldn't swallow well. He was diagnosed with esophageal cancer stage III . . . due to his thirty plus years of smoking and drinking. The surgeon gave my dad two choices: chemotherapy or surgery. According to my dad, both options were presented as comparable options. However, because he was a South Korean immigrant, there were serious language barriers . . .
>
> He chose chemotherapy. It probably was a wrong choice in hindsight, although no one could prove that. However, the option of surgery quickly disappeared when my dad lost so much weight due to the chemotherapy because he could no longer swallow food. At that point, the surgeon told us that the

surgery was too dangerous now and reprimanded my dad for not trying hard enough to eat and for making a wrong choice. I later realized that the esophagus could lose reflexes following chemotherapy, and I now understand how wrong that surgeon was in telling my dad to try to eat.

Dad was in the hospital for about two months. The insurance didn't want to pay any longer and the doctor placed my dad at the nursing home. After a month's stay in a nursing home, the insurance didn't want to pay anymore. My dad didn't want to burden me, and he chose to stay at the nursing home; it was about $10,000 per month.

After a month, I brought my dad to my home. His bank account was hitting the bottom . . . The home nurse came to our home once a week. She gave me the list of twenty drugs and instructed me what to give and when. A friend suggested getting a second opinion and introduced us to a doctor.

We were told it would cost us at least $40,000 and insurance wouldn't cover out-of-state medical costs. My dad chose not to get [a] second opinion. He wanted to live, and he tried everything from natural foods known to fight cancer, [to] supplements and acupuncture.

He became anxious as he lost more weight . . . I watched him dying on the ER bed while suffering in extreme pain. Even in his pain, he didn't forget to thank the nurse who injected the painkiller. The nurse placed her hand on my dad's forehead and told him that [it wasn't his place] to be thanking her but seemed so grateful that he did say, "Thank you."

She was the only healthcare professional who actually cared for my dad . . . during this nightmare.

Surgical Errors

In December 2008, a woman had robot-assisted laparoscopic surgery to remove a kidney that contained a large tumor. The good news was that the tumor proved to be a noninvasive papillary transitional carcinoma and had not spread to her lymph nodes or to any other adjacent tissues. She was cured.

The bad news was that immediately following the surgery she began experiencing severe abdominal pain. The physicians and nurses minimized her complaints. However, on the second day after her surgery, her blood pressure dropped, and she became hypotensive. After she looked into her husband's eyes and told him she was going to die, he called for help.

Surgeons discovered that her bowel had been nicked during her surgery, causing leakage of bowel contents into the peritoneum and into her bloodstream. Her severe abdominal pain and septic shock (blood infection causing organ dysfunction or failure and a large drop in blood pressure) had been caused by secondary peritonitis, a very dangerous and potentially fatal infection. The patient was experiencing the consequences of a surgical error.

Her infection was later complicated by respiratory failure requiring tracheal (windpipe) intubation and she was put on a mechanical respirator and moved to the Intensive Care Unit (ICU), where she remained for twenty days. Soon after being discharged, she returned within six days because of additional undrained abdominal abscesses. After multiple procedures and prolonged antibiotic treatment over two months in the hospital, she was again discharged. Open wounds finally healed six and a half months after her original surgery.

After increased activity led to large hernias, her surgeon elected to delay repair because of the recent severe illnesses. Unfortunately, due to postoperative complications, she lost her job, and soon lost her health insurance coverage. Unable to pay out-of-pocket, she applied for and received Medicare coverage, but her surgeon was fearful of operating and warned that surgery could cause further bowel damage.

Today, because of her poor bowel function, she eats a very limited diet and wears a special binder to reduce her hernias. Many physicians have discharged her from their care, saying, "You ask too many questions." Now she asks no questions and agrees with whatever the doctor says, but she wishes they would help her to fully regain her health.

Infection Following a Biopsy

At the age of five months, a baby girl was first diagnosed with retinoblastoma (a rare inherited retinal cancer) in both eyes and required two years of aggressive chemotherapy and radiation, as well as the removal of her right eye. She appeared to be cancer-free until age eight when she developed severe pain in her right upper thigh. A biopsy confirmed the worst: she had a second tumor, an osteosarcoma, a bone tumor that can accompany retinoblastoma. The good news was, if surgical tumor resection was performed immediately, her leg could be saved.

However, within 48 hours of her biopsy, she became hypotensive due to *Staphylococcus aureus* sepsis resulting in respiratory and kidney failure. She required surgical drainage of a pus collection at the biopsy site, prolonged intravenous antibiotics and ventilator support, and remained in the ICU for seven weeks, where she developed painful bedsores. The delay in resecting her tumor resulted in its continued growth until the only treatment possible was an above-the-knee amputation, two weeks after her discharge from the ICU.

Her parents were devastated but insisted, "We're not going to mourn for her while she is still alive. We'll have the rest of our lives for that. Our job is to make the most of every minute we do have."

Her last 19 months of life were extremely hard, as she suffered from severe phantom limb pain and a ventilatory function 70% of normal. She also experienced severe post-traumatic stress, frequently waking with nightmares and/or a wet bed.

Through all her suffering, this special child maintained a positive spirit and tried to look at the bright side of her predicament. After the loss of her leg, she told her parents, "You know, I will be able to walk again with a prosthetic leg. Some people lose both legs or a leg and an arm. I have it easier than they do." Her parents will never forget their courageous and beautiful daughter who died because of a postoperative wound infection that could have been prevented by proper preoperative wound site cleaning and effective sterile technique.

A Broader View

Take a pause, and then consider what these cases have in common. You likely noticed that the doctors and nurses involved often ignored the complaints of their patients and failed to consider suggestions for improved care.

For my part, these moving stories encouraged me to become an active member of the nonprofit patient advocacy organization, the Empowered Patient Coalition (EPC). The EPC was founded by Julia Hallisy following her daughter's death. Amplifying the concerns of patients was one of the organization's primary goals. To this end, Julia helped to create a detailed anonymous online survey that has enabled patients and their families to document more than 600 episodes of harm caused by medical errors.

Julia and I realized that patients and patient families were primarily talking only *to themselves*, and that the patient's view of medical errors was not being shared in the medical literature. Yet *health systems and health professionals needed to understand the personal consequences of their error-prone care.*

With the help of a graduate student in the School of Public Health at our university, we analyzed 696 online patient EPC questionnaires. (7) Data showed that the most common sources of error were errors in diagnosis and treatment (30%), second was surgical-related complications (24%), followed by hospital-acquired infections (22%), and adverse medication events (18%) (Figure 3-1).

My own experience of losing my leg and the cases just described fall into these first three categories. And in chapter 1, we saw how Mary experienced a medication error (under-dosing of heparin) as well as diagnostic and treatment delays.

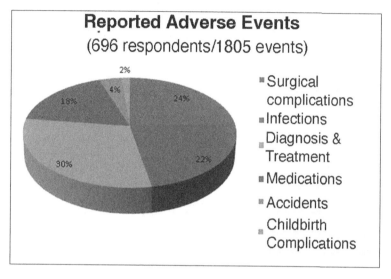

Reported Adverse Events
(696 respondents/1805 events)

- Surgical complications
- Infections
- Diagnosis & Treatment
- Medications
- Accidents
- Childbirth Complications

Figure 3-1. Breakdown of medical errors from our EPC Online Survey.

In analyzing the narratives of injured patients and their families, several major themes were also discovered. Lack of accountability was the most prominent concern, expressed by 90% of the respondents. Nearly half of the providers insisted their care was appropriate, and a similar percentage denied all responsibility for the harm patients and families had experienced. Forty percent adopted a secretive approach and avoided involving the family in their analysis of the cause of patient harm. Finally, one-third of doctors ceased all communication with the patient and family after a complaint had been filed.

Communication failure was a second major concern. As described in the cases above, there were many families and patients who didn't feel heard. They complained that their doctors didn't listen, and often reported that the doctor was disrespectful and/or intimidating.

Like my blog, the EPC survey results also conveyed the frequently devastating consequences of medical errors. One-third of patients experienced severe post-event psychological stress, one-third experienced severe financial stress, and one-third died following a medical error. In addition, nearly one-third required follow-up surgery or treatment.

What were some of the patient's and family's suggestions for improving the present sad state of affairs? Suggestions fell into three categories:

1. Standardization of care by creating reliable protocols;
2. Better coordination of care through more effective teamwork; and
3. Improved listening skills.

Finally, respondents highlighted the importance of shared decision-making and patient empowerment. Many of the errors they encountered might have been prevented if the patients' and families' opinions and concerns had been seriously considered.

Our large national survey revealed that my prior efforts at improving the quality and safety of patient care were on the right track, and this survey provided the blueprint for my future efforts to reduce medical errors and improve the quality of patient care.

Empowering Patients

The EPC survey revealed that stories like ours were unfolding throughout the United States and likely throughout the world. Our survey emphasized that the urgency of this problem had not diminished. After the survey, I founded a local branch of the EPC and recruited patients and medical students to participate. We held several public meetings to share personal stories describing the difficulties patients encounter trying to navigate our health systems. One of our goals was to encourage medical students to look through the eyes of their patients.

Hallisy and I subsequently realized that, although the number of patients killed or permanently injured was excessive, on a per capita basis these events remained rare. Unless a family member had suffered harm, however, people were not attracted to local activities such as forums and protests that focused on improving the safety of patient care. Local interest in the EPC chapter steadily declined, and we disbanded.

Beginning Again

After closing the local chapter, I sought another patient advocacy organization that was dedicated to community activism and reforming our healthcare system. A unique organization that was well organized and highly motivated was the Right Care Alliance (RCA). RCA is affiliated with the Lown Institute, a renowned "nonpartisan think tank advocating bold ideas for a just and caring system for health." Its leadership realized that in addition to a policy arm, they required a campaign arm to spread their ideas and convince the public that our present healthcare system needed reform.

The RCA membership includes patients, physicians, nurses, and other members of the lay community, and as with the EPC, patients have prominent voices in the organization. Their vision is to fight for a healthcare system that focuses on "patients over profits." Their overall goal is to promote a healthcare system that is affordable, accessible to all, incorporates local community input, and focuses on primary care.

Attending an RCA national meeting in Boston in January of 2018, I was impressed with their energy and commitment. Most important to me, the patients and lay members spoke up, and their opinions were respected by the membership. This meeting primarily focused on finalizing their first major campaign goal: highlighting the high cost of insulin and a call for a reduction in price.

For people with type I diabetes, insulin is a necessity, not a luxury. How, then, can drug companies charge over $300 per vial of insulin? In 1972, the cost of a vial was $9; in 1996, it was $36; by 2010, it rose to $112; and then it steeply increased to $275 in 2017 and to nearly $400 in 2019. So, the price increased 44-fold in 45 years and nearly tripled in ten years. The average patient requires two vials of insulin per month and, combined with glucose monitoring equipment, this made the monthly cost in 2019 nearly $1,000.

Yet the cost of manufacturing has remained low, *approximately $10 per vial.* Companies were earning outrageous profits on a medication that diabetics required *for survival.* Pharmaceutical companies justify their high charges as a requirement to support the high cost of research and development. But, ironically, in 1923 the discoverers and patent owners of insulin – Frederick Banting, Charles Best, and James Collip of the University of Toronto – sold their patent to Eli Lilly for only $1. They recognized the survival necessity of insulin to these patients and wanted to assure its availability to all. Banting stated at the time, "Insulin does not belong to me, it belongs to the world."

In the name of shareholders, this altruistic spirit was ignored, and pharmaceutical companies chose profits over patients.

As the chapter leader of RCA, I then helped to organize several forums where experts in diabetes from the medical school spoke about the importance of reducing the price of insulin. Our audience included community members, medical, pharmacy, and nursing students; physicians and nurses. We sent letters to our Congressional representatives and we wrote editorials.

Patient deaths revealed the devastating and unjust consequences of pharmaceutical companies valuing profits over patient welfare. Four of these cases were particularly poignant:

- One man died on March 18, 2017, at the age of 48. After moving to care for a parent, he lost insurance coverage for his insulin. At the time of his death from diabetic ketoacidosis (DKA), his GoFundMe campaign was just $50 short of the purchase price for his insulin. He cared for his mother until her death. The week after she died, he lost his life.
- Another young man died on February 7, 2018, at 32 years of age. In November 2017, he lost his job and could no lon-

ger afford health insurance, paying out of pocket for insulin. Rationing his insulin because the cost was too high, he died of DKA alone in his apartment.

- An even younger patient died on November 4, 2018, at the age of 26. He was a former high school wrestling star and football player and had just started a new job, but his health insurance did not activate for one month. During this time, he couldn't afford his long-acting insulin ($1,200 per month) and tried to ration a cheaper intermediate-acting insulin. He developed DKA and fell into a coma, dying just two weeks before he was to receive insurance coverage.

- A young woman died on June 22, 2019; 24 years old. Developing type 1 diabetes at age seven, she was a lifelong lover of the performing arts and had a job at a local movie theater. However, her salary was insufficient to consistently afford her medications. She was faced with a terrible choice: pay her rent or pay the $300 cost of insulin. Her solution was insulin rationing, leading to her hospitalization for DKA in early June. Soon after being discharged from the hospital, she was found dead.

On November 1st 2019, we held a candlelight vigil for people who had died trying to ration their insulin. As we read these stories, the audience held lit candles. We closed our vigil with a prayer from Father Alan Bower, our hospital chaplain and member of the RCA:

God created the world and all things in it and entrusted them into our hands so that we might use them for our good and for the building up of human society. Today we pray that God will strengthen those who in their diabetic condition face financial hardship related to their medication needs. We pray for ourselves that we may encourage and support them in the days ahead.

God of Mercy, console those who have lost loved ones due to their inability to afford the costly treatment for diabetes and support those who continue to struggle with this malady. Guide us to impress upon those who manufacture these necessary medications to reassess their marketing practices. And may the concern for the greater good soften their hearts and prompt them to provide reasonable and affordable treatment of diabetes for those so afflicted.

Amen.

In January 2023, we finally succeeded. Our chapter's insulin campaign – along with protests from many other organizations – resulted in a government mandate capping the monthly cost of insulin to $35/month for all Medicare patients. Eli Lilly, the major US manufacturer of insulin, lowered the price of insulin for the first time to $25 per vial for regular insulin and the price of long-acting insulin by 78%. We are proud that we were able to play a part in achieving this important goal.

The RCA campaign is now focusing on the high cost of US health care. Surveys reveal that four out of every ten Americans have significant medical debt (greater than $250). Americans now owe $195 billion in medical debt, which is the leading cause of bankruptcy in the US. Our system is currently rewarding waste and low-value care. Because a fee-for-service reimbursement system prevails throughout the US, the more procedures and tests performed, the higher the revenue. Under these conditions, waste reduction and focusing on high-value care results in lower bills and lost revenue.

On April 21st, 2023, we held our first on-the-ground protest. Members of the RCA shared their exorbitant medical bills with the audience and after reading the charges, each member burned their bill. The audience cheered as each medical bill was destroyed. However, we all recognized that this was a symbolic act, and that only through carefully crafted strategies and tactics can we hope to reduce the high cost of US health care.

Looking Back, Moving Ahead

Today, I have embraced community activism to stay in touch with the lay public. Also, as an American, I feel it is my duty to devote personal effort to reforming our systems. Even as a medical student at Columbia University, in 1970 I took a three-month leave of absence to campaign for Congressman Allard Lowenstein, a strong opponent of the Vietnam War, who had orchestrated the 'Dump Johnson' campaign to prevent President Lyndon B. Johnson from winning the Democratic nomination for the presidency.

At that time, marches and sit-ins were not effective, and I chose instead to try to bring about change by working within our system and applying organizing methods to elect a representative who could continually offer legislation to end the war. During the campaign, I also learned the organizing skills that I now apply in my quality improvement projects and in community outreach.

As the election outcome demonstrated – Johnson did not seek reelection and republican candidate Richard Nixon won – campaign wins are never assured! The Lowenstein campaign could not overcome the large deficit in Democratic voters created by the gerrymandering of his district. Yet, just as I felt it was my duty to responsibly campaign to end the Vietnam War, I now feel it is my moral obligation to campaign to reform our healthcare systems. As Reverend Coffin, Yale College Chaplain, warned, "Life being what it is, if we don't make a difference by trying, we will make a difference by not trying." If each of us does our small part, we may eventually make a difference.

Most importantly, working with patients and the lay public assures that I keep my eye on the honey: extraordinary and **flawless health care** for all. The tragic outcomes of cases described in this chapter should be **NEVER events.** We must demand that all healthcare systems emulate the successes of the highly coordinated system that has allowed honeybees to survive for over 100 million years. (3)

The following chapter explores how systems thinking can help.

35

Chapter 4: Becoming a Systems Thinker

Culture eats strategy for breakfast.
—Peter Drucker

In 1991, systems thinking was rare in health care and many medical centers continued to encourage physicians to act as lone practitioners. That year, I chose a new academic position because I wanted to make a difference. I accepted the position of Chief of Infectious Diseases at an up-and-coming state-funded medical school. My ambition was to spread the culture and values I had learned at Boston City Hospital and Massachusetts General Hospital, and to continue to conduct the cell biology and biochemical studies I had been performing at Harvard.

I admired the Chair of Medicine, my immediate supervisor. His vision matched mine: for our division to become the premier clinical and research-oriented infectious disease division in the Southeastern US. In addition, the Infectious Diseases Division had recently been moved to the new Academic Research Building. Not only did it provide state-of-the-art laboratories within several hundred feet of the hospital wards but – even more importantly – it brought together physician researchers from the Department of Medicine together with investigators from the basic science departments.

As an intern at Boston City Hospital, I spent time working in the clinical research building called the Thorndike Laboratory. (8) The close physical proximity of clinical and basic scientists resulted in rich collaborations and high levels of research productivity. I hoped that my new laboratory could achieve a level of productivity similar to that of the Thorndike.

I quickly established research projects with a professor of biochemistry and a professor of microbiology and immunology. The scientific teamwork I experienced was inspiring. We combined laboratory meetings, shared ideas, and together designed experiments and reviewed and interpreted our results.

During my first ten years, our laboratory joined several ideal scientific teams, and together we produced a stream of highly regarded peer-reviewed scientific papers. Our high level of creativity and productivity also allowed us to successfully compete for multiple National Institute of Health research grants that fully funded our research. In a sense, we became a mutual admiration society. As scientific teams, we built each other up and created an ideal synergy.

So far, so good.

Ethical Issues

In addition to building the laboratory and my research program, I was charged with improving our clinical program, and this proved to be a far greater challenge. Soon after arriving at the university, I attended my first infectious disease clinical conference. A pharmaceutical salesperson supplied lunch for the conference attendees. As one of the senior faculty complained that there was no Parmesan cheese, tears welled up in the salesperson's eyes. The same senior faculty member also criticized their presentation on antibiotics as being biased. Again, I saw tears begin to flow, and the salesperson left the room.

"Why was a pharmaceutical representative supplying our lunch? Wasn't this a conflict of interest?" I wondered. And why was this poor salesperson being harassed? The experience served as a warning that the culture of physicians at this state-funded university was very different from the institutions where I had trained.

I prepared a memo to our division: "We will no longer expect salespeople to provide lunch. We will continue to schedule their pre-conference presentations so that we are up to date on the latest medications and diagnostic procedures. To eliminate any possible conflict of interest, I will ask that the pharmaceutical representatives give us no gifts." The memo was met with silence. Although I had the full backing of the Chair of Medicine, I had begun my role as division chief as 'the bad guy'.

In addition to changing our clinical conferences, I was asked to improve our infectious disease consulting service. Our division was supposed to be guiding the management of all serious infections in our hospitalized patients. Imagine my surprise when I learned that, despite being a 650-bed hospital, we received only one infectious disease consultation request per day. We should have been receiving ten to fifteen consults per day.

On my first consultation with the surgical service, I was asked to assist in the treatment of a patient with a post-operative infection. I quickly realized the problem: this patient was receiving an antibiotic regimen that we had not used in ten years due to its kidney and bone marrow toxicity.

Approaching the surgical attending who was at the patient's bedside, I greeted him enthusiastically, "Hi, I am Dr. Fred Southwick the new Chief of Infectious Diseases. I look forward to assisting you in the management of your infected patients."

Instead of a warm welcome, I received a frown. Unperturbed I continued, "I recommend you switch to a newer class of antibiotic because this antibiotic class will provide better coverage with much lower toxicity."

I had expected a thank you and perhaps a request for additional clarification. Instead, he looked angrily into my eyes and yelled, "You're from ID [infectious diseases]. I hate ID!"

In this very dysfunctional culture, toxic attitudes seemed to have begun some thirty years ago when the medical school was founded.

The surgeons attracted cases because they required a significant patient volume to maintain their surgical skills. The medicine faculty initially attracted few patients and spent most of their time teaching and conducting research. Subsequently, this early model dramatically changed. The medicine faculty had since attracted a large volume of patients and worked equally hard. Stereotypes, however, had persisted.

How could I improve our consultation volume given this cultural divide? Meeting with the Chair of Surgery to inquire, I promised prompt service and close follow-up. The Chief of Surgery was very receptive. With his encouragement and the establishment of standardized expectations for all infectious disease consultants, our service quickly grew and within six months we had achieved an average of ten infectious disease consults per day.

Updating Prescription Regimens

But there remained a second problem. As I was consulted about another surgical patient with a postoperative infection, I again encountered an out-of-date toxic antibiotic regimen. The surgeon refused to change the prescription, insisting that this was the treatment they had successfully used for years.

This behavior made no sense to me until I realized I was dealing with a series of silos and a fragmented system where disrespect was the rule. If we couldn't prevent patients from receiving the wrong antibiotics through our consultation service, I realized the only option would be to mandate the appropriate therapy by creating an antibiotic stewardship program.

One of the first infectious diseases experts to institute such a program was Dr. Maxwell Finland at Boston City Hospital. His very detailed studies revealed a frightening development. With the initial release of antibiotics, there was a dramatic drop in the death rate from sepsis from 58% in 1935 to 30% in 1947. However, over the ensuing decade, mortality climbed back up to 38%, and he found that the bacteria grown from the blood cultures in 1957 were nearly all resistant to sulfa and penicillin antibiotics. (9)

Thus, in the 1970s, experts were concerned that we were approaching 'antibiotic Armageddon' or the 'end of the antibiotic era'. Antibiotic restriction programs were and continue to be regarded as the primary tool to protect us from this devastating outcome. (10) In 1973, as an intern at Boston City Hospital, I was not allowed to prescribe antibiotics without permission from our Infectious Diseases Division. By reserving new antibiotics only for patients who had developed serious infections, antibiotic restriction programs (now called antibiotic stewardship programs) could reduce the frequency of what are now called multi-drug resistant (MDR) bacteria.

I contacted our Chief Medical Officer and proposed initiating an antibiotic stewardship program, pointing out that this program would reduce the selection of multi-drug resistant (MDR) bacteria, shorten hospital stays (because infections would improve more quickly if all patients received the most effective antibiotics), and most importantly save lives. He enthusiastically embraced the concept. In 1994, it was exciting to be part of one of the first Southeastern medical centers to be instituting an antibiotic stewardship program.

Backlash

In retrospect, my first quality improvement project portended a challenging future. The program was announced in the hospital bulletin, and within three days, staff physicians were furious. "Academic freedom dictates that I can prescribe any antibiotic I want!" declared one angry surgeon. (However, with one or two exceptions, none of our surgeons had any infectious disease training.) The surgeons immediately began boycotting infectious disease consultations. Our volume dropped from ten to two or three consults per day. The Chief Medical Officer was deluged with complaints.

During the second week of our restriction policy, I encountered an unjustified use of antifungal medication and when I attempted to enforce our restrictions, I was met with anger and name-calling.

After three weeks, the Chief Medical Officer gave in and discontinued the stewardship program. "We aren't ready for this change," he reported to me in a sad tone as he shrugged his shoulders and stared at the floor.

Altogether, it took our hospital more than *three decades* to follow Dr. Finland's example. Our stewardship program was not fully instituted until 2006, twelve years after our first effort, and it took another eleven years (in 2017) for the Joint Commission on Accreditation of Healthcare Organizations (JCAHO) – the body responsible for certifying hospitals – to mandate antibiotic restriction policies.

A Persistent Condition

The snail's pace for the acceptance of new treatments and procedures in health care remains a major impediment to improving patient safety.

On average, it takes 17 years for research findings to be adopted in clinical practice. Stewardship programs, being system-wide, have taken over twice as long to be adopted. (10)

At our hospital, despite the attempted implementation of our antibiotic stewardship program, we continued to see high levels of MDR bacteria infecting patients. Several patients had died of infections. Could we reduce these rates? In 2006, I recruited a highly experienced, multidisciplinary team to join a task force, and we kicked off the first meeting of the Resistant Pathogen Task Force.

At that time, one of the major sites for MDR bacterial infection was in the lungs of patients requiring mechanical ventilation, which is termed ventilator associated pneumonia (VAP). In our intensive care units (ICUs), all patients who had opacities on chest X-ray underwent bronchoscopy (the placement of a fiberoptic tube in the bronchi or air channels of the lung) to obtain bacterial cultures, a procedure called bacterial alveolar lavage (BAL).

The prestigious *New England Journal of Medicine* (NEJM) published a large, randomized study in 2006 that compared this approach with simple suctioning of the upper airway of the lungs. No differences in the organisms that were cultured, antibiotics administered, or clinical outcomes were observed between the two groups. (11) Subsequently, two detailed analyses in 2014 and 2020 confirmed that endotracheal (upper airway) suction samples are comparable to invasive BAL samples in terms of organisms cultured, antibiotic use, and clinical outcomes in patients with VAP. (12, 13) In other words, BAL did *not* produce better outcomes than suctioning.

Armed with our own observational studies and the NEJM findings, our task force recommended that BAL cultures no longer be performed in cases of VAP. Yet, as we predicted, the head of the ICU reacted negatively, and two days later we received notification from the Chief Medical Officer that BAL cultures would be continued in our ICUs. Deeply disappointed, the task force agreed that continuing to meet served no purpose and was disbanded.

Embracing Systems Thinking

Although healthcare complexity was dramatically increasing, and the need for the coordination of care and teamwork was becoming critical, I still lacked an understanding of the challenges of cultural divides. In hindsight, many of our challenges could have been described or predicted with systems thinking:

- In our healthcare center, two beehives (systems) were actively competing against each other for nectar and pollen. For instance, the Chief Medical Officer (Hive One) was one of the surgeons who had previously refused to follow our infectious disease consultant's antibiotic recommendations. Why was I surprised, then, that he ignored the Resistant Pathogen Task Force's (Hive Two) recommendations? Their goals and values were not aligned.
- I might have applied the concept of adaptive change or the beekeeper analogy (more about that in chapter 6).
- Working within each system, we might have used orga-

nizing methods to identify potential champions within each system and encouraged them to convince their fellow surgeons to change their procedures.

Improving the quality of care in our medical center would require a better understanding of the cultural challenges, as well as a new set of skills, to bring about the changes we so badly needed. Therefore, in 2007 I attended the Harvard Macy Institute conference entitled "Leading Innovation in Health Care and Education."

The Medical Hive: A Systems View

At the conference, speaker Steven Spear explained how the Toyota Production System (TPS) – a methodology initially used in vehicle manufacturing to drastically increase production system efficiency and quality control and decrease waste – could be applied to health care. As I listened, tears welled up in response to a feeling of deep sorrow and embarrassment. For 19 years, I had been blaming the physicians who first cared for Mary for her near-death and, like a bolt of lightning, I now instantly realized my error.

As Spear described how an integrated system approach could dramatically reduce errors and improve efficiency in health care, the realization suddenly hit me that Mary's near-death experience was not simply the consequence of bad doctors, but primarily caused by woefully deficient *systems* of care. Yes, the physicians who first took care of Mary had some personal responsibility for the events that had unfolded, but they were also *victims of dysfunctional systems.*

At the same time, I felt a sense of renewal and excitement. This was it. This was the blueprint for achieving safe and high-quality medical care! Just as TPS had revolutionized the auto industry by progressively improving the quality of automobiles, it could revolutionize health care. And applying TPS to health care could prevent future cases like Mary's from happening.

At the end of the talk, I rushed up to Steve. Red-eyed and shaken, I thanked him for his thoughtful and transformational presentation.

I then read several books describing how to implement TPS as well as Spear's paper in the *Harvard Business Review* entitled "Learning to Lead at Toyota."(14)

My childhood experience also encouraged me to read extensively about the integrated system created by honeybees. Unlike many insects, including many other bees, honeybees do not hibernate during the winter, but remain active using the energy from honey to continually contract their flight muscles, generating the heat required to warm the closely packed and insulated winter nest. Thanks to honey, the average beehive of 80,000 bees can maintain temperatures above 50°F, even when outside temperatures drop to as low as -20°F. (3) This means that to weather the winter, the average beehive must store a minimum of 55 lbs. of honey and an additional 77 lbs. of honey to maintain the caloric needs of the colony during the summer. (3)

Over 100 million years, the honeybee has developed a highly coordinated system to maximize the chances that the bee colony can produce sufficient life-sustaining honey. This system requires the orchestration of four million foraging trips, flying a total distance of twelve million miles. (3) No wonder each worker bee appears so focused and efficient as they gather nectar.

I believed that the honeybee hive as well as TPS could provide the guiding principles for efficient high quality safe health care. Transparency – the sharing of all errors – would be a key principle. If those who work within a system hide their errors, there can be no improvement. I eventually wrote a rebuttal to my original paper called "Who was Caring for Mary, Revisited." *Academic Medicine* agreed to consider the piece. Then I contacted Steve Spear.

Together we performed a systems analysis of each step in Mary's illness (Figure 4-1). (15) Our analysis broke Mary's hospitalization into nine stages and revealed six major themes:

1. Firstly, the entire cascade of events was triggered by prescribing amoxicillin without a careful family history (FH) that would have revealed severe allergic reactions to penicillin (Figure 4-1, Stage 1).

2. Secondly, the care in the early phases of her illness lacked continuity. The neurologist was the first to drop her care when he left for a conference (Figure 4-1, Stage 3). In an ideal system, he would have transferred her care to a second neurologist, who could have orchestrated hospitalization and focused on the primary early manifestation of vasculitis, which was neuropathy. Care was also dropped by the first internist, as she provided a rushed sign-out by phone (Figure 4-1, Stage 4).

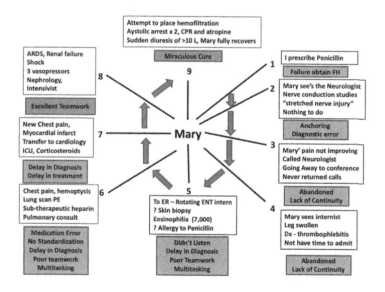

Figure 4-1. The stages of Mary's illness. ARDS, acute respiratory distress syndrome. CPR, cardiopulmonary resuscitation. FH, family history. Dx, diagnosis. ER, emergency room. PE, pulmonary embolism. CCU, Cardiac Care Unit.

3. A third major problem was diagnostic error and treatment delay. The neurologist anchored on the diagnosis of physical damage to the nerves caused by her job as a dance instructor. He ignored the negative MRI, failed to generate a list of other possible diagnoses and failed to order tests to look for alternative explanations (Figure 4-1, Stage 2). Next, the intern and faculty member who admitted her to the hospital strictly focused on her thrombophlebitis and ignored the dark blisters that were highly likely to have been manifestations of vasculitis. They were aware of the very high eosinophil counts, but despite recommendations from hematology, they never ordered corticosteroids (Figure 4-1, Stages 5-7).

4. A fourth major problem was the failure to use a standardized protocol to manage the intravenous heparin administration, explaining the under-dosing of heparin. The nurses could have assisted in managing the rate of intravenous infusion if the proper protocol had been in place (Figure 4-1, Stage 6).

5. Fifthly, rather than an interdependent team in which everyone continually communicated and worked together, the physicians worked separately, fulfilling their individual tasks, and did not share the workload or responsibility (Figure 4-1, Stages 5 and 6). Mary might instead have been considered the team's patient rather than the novice intern's patient, and everyone would have pitched in to help fill out flow sheets, making suggestions for her care and integrating the input from the consultant physicians. Teamwork was also absent when it came to the nurses and consultants. Conversations with the nurses revealed that they were clearly aware of Mary's subtherapeutic heparin dosing, but failed to relay this message because they feared doctors would interpret their communication as being 'disrespectful'. The consults also were never incorporated into

the team and consequently, their recommendations were never integrated into the management plan.

6. Finally, the faculty attending was required to multitask – an all-too-common expectation in academic medical centers. In addition to supervising Mary's care and the other 15 patients on the team's service, he was required to continue his administrative duties as a division chief and to continue to supervise his active clinical research program (Figure 4-1, Stages 5 and 6). Through their work expectations, the university medical center had inadvertently created a culture where patients were of secondary importance.

Based on our analysis, we concluded that **teamwork** was the most vital component of effective, safe, high-quality medical care.

Working Together

I wondered, "When I serve as the ward attending, are my residents, interns, medical students, nurses and I working as a true team?"

The answer to this question was a resounding, "No." On rounds, I rarely interacted with nurses, and in most cases, rather than soliciting opinions from other team members, I encouraged only the intern primarily responsible for each patient to talk. Our discussions were also conducted in the hallway, purposely excluding the patient. After each discussion, we briefly said hello to our patients and informed them of our plan for the day. We did not solicit their opinions and discouraged questions to save time. Thus, I too was promoting a working group rather than a working *team*.

Could the basic principles of TPS be applied to improve the efficiency and effectiveness of work rounds?"

Yes, they could. First, our team would need to continually ask whether each activity on rounds was of value to the patient. 'Value' was defined as an activity, test, or procedure that significantly improved the health and well-being of the patient. If so, then the activity is of value. If not, then the activity is of nonvalue, i.e., it is waste and should be eliminated.

For example, long monologues by the senior physicians about the underlying causes of each patient's disease and the many manifestations of their illness were of limited value. On the contrary, long bedside teaching sessions during 'management' or work rounds seriously delayed patient care. It often extended work rounds by several hours, postponing the ordering of consultations, medications, and diagnostic tests. Instead, this activity could be performed after work rounds.

In addition to removing wasteful activity, TPS is guided by three key principles:

1. Create and follow protocols or job descriptions that clearly define each person's role on the team. All tasks must be described in sufficient detail so that a novice following the instructions would behave like an expert.

2. All customer-supplier relationships must be specified regarding the specific needs of the customer and should include time and communication expectations.

3. Everyone involved in providing the service or product is empowered to apply the scientific method to suggest improvements.

Applying these principles to work rounds, I wrote job descriptions for each member of the team including the patients and nurses. I next reviewed the key customer-supplier relationships, initially focusing on the most important relationships for our team: the doctor-patient and doctor-nurse relationships.

What should the ideal relationships look like? If the patient is viewed as the owner of the process and care is truly patient-centered, the team needs to supply each patient with the latest information about their illness and try to explain the rationale behind their treatments. To accomplish this, the team needs to perform rounds *at the bedside* and present current information to the patient and the patient's family. In this way, everyone will be on the same page. Because who will be taking care of the patient upon discharge from the hospital? The patient and family will be managing the illnesses. It's therefore essential for them to understand what treatments are being ordered and why they are being given.

Bedside nurses interact with their patients repeatedly during their 12-hour shifts, and the bedside nurse is the team member that provides the bulk of each patient's care. Therefore, this team member must be supplied with complete, clear, and concise instructions regarding each medication and expected nursing interventions. If the nurse doesn't understand the plans for the day, the patients won't receive the care they require. The most effective way to convey new management plans is face-to-face, and the physicians on the team should be prepared to answer any questions. By the completion of bedside rounds, the nurse should have a full understanding of the patient's management plans.

To assure efficient use of time, a standardized communication protocol is followed that relays the current patient complaints; lists the most recent physical examination, laboratory, and imaging findings; relays the presenter's impression of how the patient is doing (Is the patient getting better, getting worse, or staying the same?); and finally reviews the management plans for the day (What tests did the presenter recommend and why? What new medications are going to be started or changed and why?).

To encourage continual improvement at the end of each work round session, as the attending, I planned to ask, "What went well?", and "What could be improved?" This gives permission for everyone on the team to make suggestions for improvement that can be incorporated into future rounds.

Sharing How TPS Applies to Health Care

After creating this new standardized approach to work rounds, I presented my plan to the faculty and trainees of the Department of Medicine at our weekly Medical Grand Rounds in a talk entitled: "Application of Toyota Production System Principles to Health Care."

When I finished the presentation, I was met with silence. Members of the audience were frowning and shaking their heads:

- "No."
- "Patients aren't cars."
- "Creating these protocols is cookbook medicine."
- "Who wants to follow a Japanese company?"
- "Health care is an art that requires the individual practitioner to be creative and make continual adjustments customized to each patient's unique needs."

They felt that education on the wards should consist of the experienced physicians taking trainees under their wings as apprentices and allowing each trainee to "watch one, do one, and then teach one." The model they espoused was a hierarchy with the senior faculty physician at the top and subsequent rungs on the ladder determined by the seniority of each trainee. The nurse and patient should remain at the very bottom.

And so, in 2008, paternalistic, inefficient, individualistic, error-prone medicine was alive and well at our medical center, as well many other academic medical centers in the US

Perhaps I should have introduced my fellow faculty to the honeybees.

Emulating Worker Bees

The coordination of 80,000 bees is as challenging as coordinating the workers within a hospital system, and every worker bee has a defined role. (3) The largest number of worker bees serve as foragers harvesting nectar and pollen. Once the foraging bees arrive at the nest, they are greeted by worker bees responsible for guarding the beehive entrance against unwanted intruders.

After passing by the guards, they hand their liquid nectar off to the receiver worker bees by mouth-to-mouth contact. The receiver bees convert the nectar to honey and then regurgitate the honey into empty hexagons in the nest honeycomb. A fourth group of worker bees clean the hexagonal honeycombs to assure the honeycombs are suitable for storage.

A fifth group is assigned to groom and feed the queen bee. This single queen bee is responsible for populating the hive by releasing 1,500 eggs per day. A sixth group of workers feeds and cares for the drones, the male bees responsible for fertilizing the queen bee's eggs. Without the care and support of worker bees the queen and drones could not survive, the colony would quickly die, and new bee colonies could not be created.

The worker bee's roles change over time and these changes are genetically programmed. Beginning in the first one to two weeks of life, they are responsible for cleaning the nest and feeding the developing nymph bees. They then become nest entrance guardians or processors of arriving nectar, groomers and feeders of the queen bee or drones. Finally, in the last one to two weeks of their 30-day life span, they become foragers assigned to find the pollen and nectar to maintain the hive's food supply.

Worker bees require no supervision and no monitoring of their performance. Their behaviors are genetically determined and the system works from the bottom-up. (2, 4) Imagine if a significant percentage of worker bees refused to harvest nectar. The bee colony would die. Thus, the honeybee colony system has evolved over 100 million years to maximize survival.

We in health care should also embrace specific job assignments because without such standardization, we endanger the lives of our patients. Our honey should always be effective, efficient, safe, and patient-centered care. TPS makes possible the creation of an integrated human system within three to five years, far quicker than the 100 million years that was required to perfect the honeybee's system.

Based on my understanding of the honeybee system, the implementation of a TPS rounding system had the potential to save lives. How could I implement TPS without using automobile assembly line analogies?

Yet the far greater challenge would be overcoming the status quo.

Chapter 5: Applying TPS to Medicine, First Try

The right hand has to know what the left hand is doing. You must have alignment.

—Coach Stephen Addazio

Following my grand rounds presentation on the application of the Toyota Production System (TPS) to healthcare delivery, I was extremely discouraged. I may have seen the light, but my fellow physicians didn't understand. How could I relay these important principles in a more palatable form?

The Toyota Production System

Ironically, TPS was not a Japanese invention – it was developed by an American, W. Edward Deming. As a Bell Laboratory engineer, he worked with his mentor, William Shewhart to develop manufacturing principles that assured the highest quality communications equipment. Much of Bell's equipment was buried underground, making repair of malfunctioning equipment labor-intensive and costly, so manufacturing reliable, high-quality equipment was of the highest priority.

Together, Deming and Shewhart created the 'System of Profound Knowledge', consisting of four elements:

1. **Understand the system or systems you are working in.** They defined a system as an interdependent group of items, people, or processes working together to achieve a common purpose. They emphasized the importance of everyone sharing the same purpose and understanding the interdependent relationships within the system.

2. **Understand variation within the system.** Everything we observe in life varies, and there are two types of variation: common cause variation (defined as a random or chance variation) and specific cause variation (defined as a change directly attributable to an intervention). When trying to improve a process, it is important to monitor the performance or outcome measure over time to determine whether 'improvement' results in specific cause variation or continues to vary randomly.

3. **Build knowledge.** This means using the scientific method to generate a hypothesis, test the hypothesis, and measure the outcome to determine whether the theory was correct. Deming and Shewhart simplified this for those working in production factories (who often had only a high school education) to apply 'plan-do-study-adjust' cycles. 'Plan' incorporates the hypothesis and experimental design into one step, 'Do' consists of implementing the new protocol or method, 'Study' consists of measuring the outcome, and 'Adjust' refers to adjusting the process by incorporating the improvement if the hypothesis is supported by the outcome measure. This was applied science.

4. **Consider the human side of change.** We need to look through the eyes of those who will need to change the way they perform a procedure or provide a service. How will they react to the change? Quality improvement leaders who ignore the human side of change do so at their peril.

At the end of World War II, Deming presented his system of quality improvement to the American automobile industry. Just as I had done, for example, when presenting grand rounds on health systems improvement, Deming falsely assumed that these companies would eagerly embrace this logical and proven method for improving the quality of their cars and trucks. At that time, US companies were making unprecedented profits and 'succeeding' using their current manufacturing approaches. They were not interested.

So, in 1950 Deming traveled to Japan. The Japanese manufacturing sector was in disarray. The quality of their products was notoriously poor and, compared to US manufacturers, it was estimated that nine Japanese workers were required to equal the output of one US worker. Aware of their poor performance, the Toyota automobile company eagerly embraced Deming's system, and the outcome was remarkable.

By the early 2000s, *Consumer Reports* rated Toyota's cars as best buys and rarely recommended US-built cars. A Consumer Union analysis at the time revealed that an eight-year-old Toyota was equivalent in reliability to a three-year-old Ford or Chrysler and a two-year-old Volkswagen. (16)

Toyota steadily increased its market share, and in 2008 the Toyota Motor Corporation became the largest manufacturer of automobiles in the World, surpassing General Motors for the first time. The US and European manufacturers quickly realized the need to match Toyota's quality and reliability. Starting in the late 2000s, every company began embracing a version of TPS under the generic name 'Lean'. Consequently, by 2015 the quality of nearly all cars and trucks had dramatically improved.

One measure of the change in the quality is the prevalence of 'lemons', new cars that demonstrate significant defects within the first weeks of being driven. In the 1970's, lemons were frequent; among the most notorious was the 1971 Ford Pinto that burst into flames if rear-ended. This serious defect resulted in multiple deaths. The Pinto also suffered from brake and transmission issues. The

AMC 1970 Gremlin had an engine that continually broke down and this model proved to be the beginning of the end for the American Motors Corporation. Also notorious was the 1960 Chevrolet Corvair, highlighted by Ralph Nader as the most dangerous car on the road because of its unconventional suspension that resulted in oversteering and frequent accidents.

By 1980, nearly every state had created 'Lemon Laws' that required the manufacturer to compensate the buyer or take back the car and refund the purchase price. The exact number of lemons per year in the US is not well documented, but a recent report demonstrates the power of TPS to eliminate lemons. The Consumers for Auto Reliability and Safety (CARS) Foundation and Frontier Group released a report of all Lemon Law litigations in California by car manufacturers from 2018-2021. (17)

The report found that General Motors led all auto manufacturers in lawsuits, with one litigation per 78 cars; Chrysler/Fiat was second with 1 per 107; Ford Motor Company fifth (1 per 148); Volkswagen eighth (1 per 304); BMW twelfth (1 per 369); and Volvo fourteenth (1 per 575). But Toyota had the *fewest litigations of all car manufacturers* with one for every 2,029 cars.

General Motors had a 26-fold higher rate of Lemon Law litigation compared to Toyota!

Applications to Health Care

This outcome can be logically extended to health care. **Preventable deaths and injuries caused by medical errors are health care's lemons**. As in Mary's case, most serious patient injuries and deaths from medical errors could be prevented.

The realization that TPS applied to health care has the potential to eliminate nearly all 'healthcare lemons' should inspire all health systems to adopt this highly effective integrated system and move from a reactive to a proactive approach to assure consistent high quality, safe patient care. I was and continue to be convinced that a fully integrated health system guided by TPS could achieve this.

My understanding of honeybee systems, which have evolved over millions of years to accumulate stores of honey, further supports this belief.

'Suiting Up'

In 2008 when I dipped my toes into the water and introduced TPS to our Department of Medicine, it was met with strong resistance (see Element Four: Consider the human side of change, above).

Experts on implementing change recommend, whenever possible, to build on an institution's strengths. Any sports fan, for example, can appreciate this in terms of the conditions required to create a championship team. These skills and practices can often be understood as reflecting TPS principles; for example, a successful football team requires:

- A highly coordinated defense and offense requires every player to know their role by studying playbooks *–adoption of protocols.*
- Perfect hand-offs and passes – the quarterback must place the ball where the receiver can most effectively catch or grasp the ball. The equivalent of *establishing customer-supplier relationships.*
- Reviewing game films (reviewing video recordings of the game) to learn what each player did well and what skills could be improved – *continual improvement guided by the scientific method.*

Let's look at a specific example. The coordination and timing of the 'Trap Play' is among the most challenging in football (Figure 5-1). The offensive tight end and tackle block the defensive tackle, leaving the defensive end unblocked. Accelerating to full speed allows the pulling guard to knock the opposing defensive end out of position with maximum force. Next, the running back can use that wide-open hole to gain ten to twenty yards, potentially scoring a touchdown.

Executing this play successfully – like healthcare teams and worker honeybees – requires perfect timing and coordination of all players. Otherwise, players trip over each other, and the play fails.

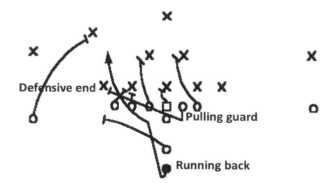

Figure 5-1. The Trap Play (x = defense, o= offense). The two circles on the left side of the line are the offensive tight end and tackle. They both block the defensive tackle, leaving the defensive end unblocked. The pulling guard drives the defensive end out of the space creating a large hole.

Another metaphor that may be helpful for musicians is to consider a musical score as a detailed protocol. It describes the intricate customer-supplier relationships between different instruments, enabling the blending of notes to create both harmony and synchronous timing. Feedback for improvement is provided both by the conductor and listening back to recordings, and difficult sections are rehearsed until the harmony and timing match the musical score.

The Athletics-Based Interprofessional Rounding (AIR) System

To apply TPS to my healthcare system, in 2009, I enthusiastically began creating an **A**thletic-based **I**nter-professional **R**ounding (AIR) system. I applied the principles of TPS to a football analogy, hoping to inspire our team of attending physicians, residents, nurses, and students to aspire to the levels of performance achieved by a championship sports team. We too could become national champions!

The first goal was to create a playbook for each role: coach, team owner, quarterback, running back, offensive line, red-shirt freshman and assistant coach.

Coach

The supervising faculty member or attending physician serves as the coach. Their goal is to help each member of the team steadily improve their performance and develop a winning team that rapidly and effectively improves the health and well-being of each patient. The coach is expected to be on the front lines closely observing the progress of the team's patients and suggesting changes if the patient isn't improving. The coach has six performance goals:

1. Facilitate communication among team members.
2. Encourage problem-solving on rounds.
3. Encourage nurses and the case manager to participate in rounds.
4. Closely adhere to a rounding schedule or game plan.
5. Encourage work sharing among members of the team.
6. Know the key clinical details for each patient prior to rounds by reviewing the electronic records each morning.

In addition, a coach should model humility and emphasize that they don't always have the answers.

Team owner

The patient and family are designated as the team owners, emphasizing the central role of the patient as the team member with the final say. As such, the patient and family can relieve the coach of their duties if the team is failing. The 'owners', physicians, and nurses share symptoms, test results, and provide input when making management decisions. When patients are severely ill, their decision making may be compromised. Under these circumstances a patient advocate (a close friend or family member) should be appointed to fulfill this role.

Quarterback

The senior resident is the leader on the field, with the guidance of the coach. They primarily lead the discussion on work rounds. They assign patients to the interns and closely supervise their performance. The quarterback must always be in close communication with the coach.

Running backs

The interns are assigned specific patients. They directly 'carry the ball', being responsible for writing all prescription and diagnostic orders as well as ordering and communicating with specialty consultants. They report to both the quarterback and coach and should continually focus on improving the health and well-being of their patients.

Offensive line

The bedside nurses are predominantly responsible for the direct care of each patient. Therefore, physicians must inform the bedside nurse of the management plans for the day. The nurse also shares all nursing observations over the past twelve hours with the other team members, relaying changes in the mental and psychological state of the patient, as well as vital sign values.

Red-Shirt Freshman

The medical student's job is to read and learn as much as possible about their patients. They don't write orders and should not be asked to perform tasks that fail to enhance their learning. Students are encouraged to spend extra time with their patients to more deeply understand the challenges that patients face.

Assistant coaches

The case manager and pharmacist fill these roles. The case manager creates the discharge plan for each patient, in close collaboration with the attending, senior resident, intern, and bedside nurse. They also order home equipment and generate referrals to rehabilitation and nursing home facilities. The pharmacist assists with medication choices and dosing, reviewing new medication orders to prevent errors.

Game Plan and Schedule

We also created a game plan and a guiding schedule for the AIR system, which predicted the time we would arrive at each patient's bedside. The time required to discuss each patient was estimated with the goal of completing rounds within two hours. On average, we had twelve active patients on our service who required day-to-day decision-making, meaning we could allot an *average* of ten minutes per patient.

At the start of each new rotation, the attending emphasizes the importance of everyone sharing their ideas and repeatedly emphasizes that every idea is valued. This approach flattens the hierarchy and encourages participation by all team members, establishing a zone of psychological safety where everyone feels comfortable sharing their ideas and sometimes disagreeing. Forming a huddle, the team is expected to encircle the bed as the intern presents the findings and plans for the day *to the patient*. Everyone hears the same facts at the same time and makes eye contact.

'Field Conditions'

In November of 2009, after sharing our set of paper playbooks and a full description of AIR, the Chief of Medicine gave permission to begin the trial to compare the effectiveness of our standardized rounds to the random and varied approaches used on the other internal medicine ward teams.

Conditions 'on the field' – in retrospect, unsurprisingly – meant that implementation was not as simple as hoped. Verbal descriptions of the rounding system were insufficient. To assure faithful adherence, I rounded with each experimental team for the first two or three days, serving as an external coach. I also taught our case manager how to evaluate the performance of each attending, and over time, she took over my coaching role.

Initially, several attendings dominated the conversation and shared large numbers of teaching points, thereby delaying decisions and wasting the nurse and case manager's valuable time. The standardized approach was an anathema to the 'academic freedom' of these faculty members.

At this point, resistance to AIR became fierce. The Chief Resident, the Training Director, and the Chair of Medicine were either openly critical or disengaged. Both the Chief Resident and Training Director were strong defenders of the status quo (often termed laggards, see chapter 6 – 'What all Beekeepers Know'). The right hand was working against the left hand, and the pilot failed 'on take-off'.

'Reviewing the Game Films'

My impatience had exacerbated their resistance. In hindsight, attempting to implement AIR might have been a better learning experience if I had approached it with greater prudence. In retrospect, two improvements might have led to more success: a clearer emphasis on how implementing the system would significantly reduce the time required for patient care, and dedicating more time to discussing and addressing resistance as it arose.

In other words, using smoke to calm the honeybees.

Chapter 6: Becoming an Adaptive Leader

There is nothing more difficult to carry out, nor more doubtful of success, nor more dangerous to handle than to initiate a new order of things. For the reformer has enemies all who profit by the old order, and only lukewarm defenders in all those who would profit from the new order. This lukewarmness arises partly from fear of their adversaries who have the law in their favor; and partly from the incredulity of mankind, who do not truly believe in anything new until they have had actual experience of it.
—Nicolo Machiavelli

After my first unsuccessful attempt at implementing the Athletic-based Inter-professional Rounding (AIR) system, in early 2010, I reviewed its design in scientific terms and was convinced we had the correct protocols to make it work on the wards. The problem was that a fifth of the more strident physicians on the team insisted on doing it their own way, making our experiment impossible to conduct.

How could I overcome these daunting challenges?

The Advanced Leadership Initiative (ALI)

In December of 2008, I read about a new fellowship at the Harvard Business School called the Advanced Leadership Initiative

(ALI). Its goal was to "unleash the potential of experienced leaders to help solve society's most pressing challenges." Harvard Professors Rosabeth Moss Kanter, Rakesh Khurana, and Nitin Nohria envisioned a "third stage of education to prepare experienced leaders, in the period of their lives once called 'retirement,' for service activities addressing societal problems."

Fellows could audit any class at Harvard during the first semester and were expected to design a project that would demonstrate how they would use their new knowledge and skills to solve a serious societal problem.

In 2000, the Institute of Medicine (now called the National Academy of Medicine) published a report estimating that preventable medical errors were responsible for 44,000 to 98,000 deaths per year in the United States. When these estimates were published many questioned the data; however, subsequent estimates now claim that 210,000 to 440,000 die each year following preventable medical errors, making it *the third leading cause of death in the US.* Even more profound, the data revealed that for every death, there were ten severe, life-altering injuries, i.e., between one and four million injuries per year.

In June 2009, I applied and was accepted to the ALI fellowship, 37 years after graduating from medical school. What a pleasure to be back on the other side of the classroom, once again the student. After six months of studying, I had learned four major principles that I could immediately apply to my efforts at health system improvement:

1. Creating highly functional teams.
2. Understanding the nature of random variation.
3. Applying the organizing methods of politicians to bring about change in large groups.
4. Understanding and leading adaptive change, changes in the way work is done.

Teamwork during Medical Work Rounds

During a Harvard Business School teamwork course, I received permission to have four groups of three students observe work rounds at one of the Harvard hospitals. I also asked that the students provide me with copies of their papers and their observations. The four groups drew very similar conclusions. For example:

- The people participating on rounds consisted of working groups rather than working teams. Individuals worked in parallel and assumed their efforts would be integrated through the hospital chart.

- They did not demonstrate collaborative decision-making during rounds and there were rarely open discussions related to the patient's management. In nearly all cases, the interns with primary responsibility for the patients turned their backs on the rest of the group and presented only to the senior physician attending.

- The content and duration of intern presentations varied greatly. Some elaborated the past medical history in detail, others focused primarily on the present active problems.

- Some members of the group did not actively participate. They often appeared distracted and at times were performing other tasks including, in one case, reading a magazine.

- The power structure was a steep hierarchy with the senior attending physician at the top, followed by the senior resident, then the interns, medical students, pharmacist and – at the bottom – was the bedside nurse. The patient was not even included in the team because all discussions took place in the hallway, ostensibly out of earshot.

- This steep hierarchy discouraged verbal input by those at the bottom of the pyramid. Nurses and pharmacists rarely spoke, and the other trainees never made suggestions about the management of cases because it was understood that they were not supposed to comment on patients that weren't their primary responsibility.

- The senior attending made all decisions, and in no case did the students witness their decisions being questioned by the other members of the rounding group. Two business students from separate observation teams shared the same comment: "I hope I never have to be hospitalized."(18)

These studies documented the great variation in rounds and lack of teamwork at this renowned Harvard hospital – just as I had observed at our university.

Deming's Red Bead Experiment

During an undergraduate course on healthcare quality that we attended as part of the ALI fellowship, we performed an eye-opening exercise whose lessons I apply almost daily. This 'Red Bead Experiment' was originally created by W. Edward Deming.

A company manufactures white beads. Workers are asked to select white beads from a mixture of red and white beads. For every five white beads there is one red bead, and workers are given a spatula with 50 holes, each of which can hold a single bead. Six students are assigned as workers, two as inspectors, and one is the recorder. Management states that workers selecting three red beads or fewer will receive a bonus; those with ten or more will be placed on probation.

The beads are thoroughly mixed and then the workers start dipping their spatulas into the mixture.

In our experiment, only one worker selected three beads and this worker received a bonus, while another worker selected twelve beads and was placed on probation.

However, all the students quickly realized that the workers had no control over how many red beads they might collect; it was merely random variation or luck. So, although 'performance' was based on the number of red beads, *trying harder would have no impact on the number of red beads selected*. The only way to improve worker performance was for management to remove the red beads from the mixture.

In health care, we can view the red beads as system defects that lead to medical errors. Many 'red beads' – miscommunication, poor coordination of care, diagnostic delays, and misdiagnosis – could be eliminated by implementing an effective inter-professional rounding system.

Organizing for Change

To change a culture and to convince caregivers to embrace new protocols, the leader must convince them to change the way they work. Effective politicians often convince those who are not strongly committed to another candidate to vote for them by sharing a personal narrative, and this same method can be used to convince healthcare professionals to adopt a new way of doing things.

In the course Organizing People to Bring About Change, students learned about the power of personal narrative. This narrative consists of three parts:

- *The Story of Self* explains why we have been called to serve. If properly described through an effective personal narrative, these stories can touch the heart of the listener and provide strong motivation for change. All effective narratives require three basic elements: an unexpected challenge, a choice, and an outcome.

- *The Story of Us* relates our personal story to the conditions in our entire community. This story should describe why we as a community need to act and why our group has the capacity to bring about change. In the case of health care, statistics about deaths due to preventable errors, general experiences related to lack of access to care, dramatic differences in the cost of care in different geographic regions, and overall surveys of quality, can all serve to motivate our community to action. In the case of healthcare providers, the central theme should be our shared goal to improve the health and well-being of our patients.

- *The Story of Now* describes an urgent, specific condition that we as a group can correct or improve. The speaker needs to challenge the audience to act by joining the campaign or project. The goal needs to be focused and outcomes must be measurable. The goal must also have a meaningful impact and specifically address the problem or problems described in the Story of Self and the Story of Us.

The 'Story of Self' should touch the heart or arouse an emotional response. Emotions arise from the amygdala, and this site has multiple connections to the prefrontal cortex, the region of the brain where decisions are made. Signals from the amygdala render the prefrontal cortex open to new information. By touching the heart, the speaker can change the mind to embrace a new action.

Understanding and Leading Adaptive Change

In the case of improving a process in healthcare delivery, the ask is often complex and may require training and embracing a new way of doing things.

In our weekly leadership seminar, an adaptive leader was defined as "A leader who is able bring about meaningful and continual change in the face of uncertainty." (19) Two types of change were described: a) **technical change**, which applies to adding new equipment to complete an *accepted* method or procedure; and b) **adaptive change**, a true change in how things are done.

Technical changes are easier to conduct and are usually readily accepted, while adaptive change creates uncertainty and may initially create more resistance and complexity. Implementation requires frequent iterative changes or plan-do-study-adjust cycles, and critical thinking. Nearly all quality-improvement projects fall into this second category.

When a leader tries to create a new order of things, those who embrace the old way feel a sense of loss, an 'emotional disequilibrium'. They attempt to reduce this disequilibrium in two ways. Firstly, they claim that they don't have time to make the changes, promising to eventually make them, but "not right now." If no change is made, there is no sense of loss, no uncertainty and the emotional disequilibrium dissipates.

The second way is to attack the person trying to lead the change. They mischaracterize the leader's motives and watch for opportunities to criticize and complain. Because adaptive leaders create emotional disequilibrium, they are often labeled as 'troublemakers'. The result, particularly in health care, is that adaptive leaders are removed from positions of authority and a deep resistance to adaptive change persists.

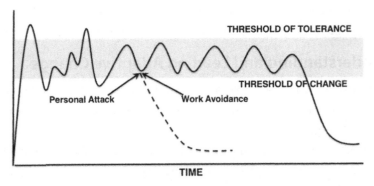

Figure 6-1. Managing emotional disequilibrium associated with adaptive change (the gray area represents the productive zone). (19)

To succeed, an adaptive leader must manage emotional disequilibrium in their team. As it increases it can become destructive, leading to protest within the group and endangering the person trying to lead the change. Adaptive leaders must be empathetic listeners, address all concerns related to the change, and emphasize the expected positive outcomes. If the emotions rise to the point that they become destructive, the adaptive leader needs to temporarily delay the change but continue to lay the groundwork for change. On the other hand, if there is no disequilibrium, then it is most likely that those being asked to change how they are working are probably not applying these changes.

In short, the adaptive leader must maintain disequilibrium in a sweet-spot called the 'productive zone', where there is not too much or too little disequilibrium. If they can maintain this level for sufficient time, the disequilibrium will resolve, and the change will become the new status quo.

In this framework, the reasons for the extreme resistance to my initial attempts to implement AIR became clear. This new way of rounding was an adaptive change. Assuming I was requesting a technical change, I had unknowingly created emotional disequilibrium and exceeded the productive zone.

For example, several internal medicine attendings believed in the paternal approach to patient care. They believed that 'the physician knows best' and that the patient should 'respect their expertise and obey' their decisions. Yet in our online Empowered Patient Coalition survey of patients who had suffered harm from preventable errors, many complained about paternalistic physicians who refused to listen. The cases in chapter 3 also demonstrate the danger of arrogant physicians who ignore the concerns of their patients. The AIR rounding system was designed to empower patients and would obviously therefore create emotional stress for those embracing the paternalistic patient care model. But because these physicians are dedicated to improving patient care, I planned to shift their perspectives by citing recent studies showing that co-management – with patients and physicians making management decisions together – improves patient satisfaction and has the potential to improve outcomes. (20, 21)

Using the AIR standardized approach, physicians were expected to listen to and show more respect toward nurses. Most importantly, this includes providing face-to-face instructions to nurses about each patient's daily management plan. Several physicians admitted they viewed nurses as inferior in their skills and knowledge and didn't want to 'waste time' speaking with them. This was another source of emotional disequilibrium and pushback.

What Beekeepers Know

Adaptive leadership is very much like a beekeeper trying to harvest honey from a beehive. It is critical that the beekeeper moves slowly so as not to upset the bees. Beekeepers also wear thick garments that block the penetration of the bee's stinger; a parallel is making sure that the leader maintains a 'thick skin'; a strong sense of purpose and self-worth. Finally, beekeepers use smoke to sooth the bees; adaptive leaders need to be empathetic listeners to sooth those who are uncomfortable with change.

Dr. Ronald Heifetz, one of our professors on the ALI program, also warned us about four mistakes that adaptive leaders often make: (19)

1. **Becoming the Chief Purpose Officer.** It is important to initially clarify the goal of the change; however, subsequently the effective adaptive leader practices restraint and primarily listens.

2. **Losing perspective.** Consider the long-term goal. During my efforts to promote the rounding program, I couldn't believe everyone wasn't jumping on board. I became overly strident. Instead, I could have asked, "What happens if we fail?" We would simply be back where we started.

3. **Becoming self-righteous.** By looking down on those who were resistant, I fell prey to this mistake as well.

4. **Becoming a martyr.** Ignoring resistance can also be a problem. If I had persisted in my efforts, rather than leaving the hospital to study at Harvard, I would likely have created many more enemies!

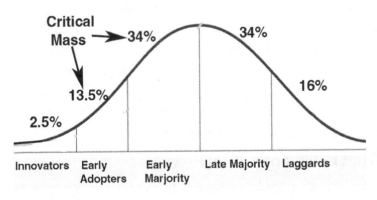

Figure 6-2. Rogers' Diffusion of Innovations uptake curve.

Looking at this dynamic in another sector, Everett Rogers studied farmers' willingness to adopt new agricultural approaches in Iowa in the 1950s. He identified five populations of farmers (Figure 6-2). (22) First were the innovators, a small percentage of farmers (2.5%), who help to create new agricultural methods. Second were the early adopters of new agricultural methods and equipment (13.5%); next were the early majority (34%), who, seeing the earlier adopters embrace change, also accepted the new methods.

Rogers also found that nearly an *equal* percentage were resistant to change. The late majority (34%) only accepted changes in agricultural innovations months after the earlier adopters and early majority. Finally, the laggards (16%), strongly resisted change and refused to adopt innovations unless mandated by the government. (22)

Rogers warned that laggards cannot be persuaded to change. He had observed that the more someone tried to persuade them, the stronger their resistance became.

This provided important guiding principles for future campaigns to bring about change in health care. In the AIR experience, a significant percentage of physicians and leaders we encountered could have been categorized as late majority or laggards. They were not comfortable with change and would not change unless mandated to do so. It is a better strategy to focus instead on the early adopters and early majority to achieve a critical mass, and then the late majority is likely to follow.

However, laggards cannot be ignored because their objections can influence the late majority and the early majority. Therefore, it is still important to listen to their complaints and attempt to directly address their concerns.

Plan: AIR Reboot

Returning to the medical center in September of 2011, I began applying my new understanding of teamwork, adaptive leadership, and organizing to re-initiate AIR. Realizing I could not do this alone, I recruited a key leader to spearhead the campaign, as well as two other faculty members and two residents. My strategy was to stay in the background and speak through the implementation team. We again assigned one team to follow the AIR system and one team followed their usual variable approach to rounding, depending on the preferences of the attending.

In addition, beginning with a personal narrative, I described to the new AIR team how poor teamwork had contributed to the medical errors and treatment delays that had nearly led to Mary's death, and how a standardized rounding program could have prevented nearly all the errors and delays she had experienced. I then shared two of my personal experiences of applying the rounding system.

Although this campaign was more effective than the first attempt, some residents and faculty continued to resist implementation behind the scenes. I experienced this resistance firsthand during an inpatient rotation. A team resident sought absolute authority in patient management, rather than closely communicating with the attending, as would be expected for a quarterback and coach. She practiced secrecy in her interactions so she that she could make decisions autonomously. Additionally, one of the two interns preferred to work alone and reported that autonomy was her primary goal.

Consequently, patient care was fragmented. We had formed a working group where members worked in parallel rather than as a team. Decisions were often doctor-centered rather than patient-centered, because the residents did not want to include their patients as part of the team. They were not receptive to suggestions for improvement.

These were the longest two weeks of my career.

In contrast, during my second two-week rotation on the same service, the team resident was collaborative, conscientious, and supportive of everyone on the team. He distributed work evenly between the two interns and did an excellent job at encouraging everyone on the team to share their ideas during rounds. I was also impressed with his humility and ability to work in the background. He continually updated me on the progress of our patients and sought advice.

The interns were thoughtful, collaborative, efficient, and effective and worked seamlessly with the team resident, embracing the standardized communication protocols. The patients were part of the team and actively participated in rounds.

During this rotation, we also took advantage of the leadership skills of one our students. She had received leadership training in the army and was very effective at creating the 'game plan' for rounds each day, leading the team to the different floors, and recruiting the bedside nurses to participate. Both students frequently discussed cases together and learned from each other as well as from the interns and team residents. Both read extensively about their patients and, to the delight of the entire team, they shared a daily factual pearl about each of their patient's illnesses.

During our two weeks together applying the AIR system, we had come together as an ideal team that provided ideal patient-centered care that was extremely efficient. The average length of hospital stay for our patients was more than 50% shorter than the other teaching teams. In other words, thanks to fully implementing the AIR system, we had more than doubled our productivity as compared to the other teams.

Do: Building on Early Success

Following these early successes, in October 2011, three months after the start of the new trial, we added a 'team launch' at the beginning of each new rotation, so that everyone understood how the team would be working together. (16) This eight-step process usually took no longer than 15 to 20 minutes – time well spent to assure the team's efforts were effectively coordinated.

1. Everyone **introduces themselves** and describes their primary learning goals for the next two-week rotation.
2. The **goals** of the team are discussed. In addition to providing highly effective, efficient, safe patient care, the attending emphasizes the measurable goal: complete work rounds in under two hours.

3. Everyone is then asked to **review their playbook** to con-firm that they understand their roles within the team.

4. Standardized communication **protocols** are agreed upon. A 'Subjective, Objective, Assessment, Plan' (SOAP) pre-sentation framework is used to describe how the patient is progressing. Subjective complaints related to the patient's illness are presented first, followed by objective findings (vital signs such as pulse, BP, RR, and temperature), phys-ical findings, laboratory findings, and imaging results. For 'assessment', the presenter summarizes how the patient is progressing. Are they better or worse? Is the progression of the disease typical for the diagnosis? Finally, the manage-ment plans for the day are listed.

5. **Milestones** are described by the attending; the primary expectation being that, by the third or fourth day of the rotation, rounds are completed within two hours.

6. **Behavioral norms** are a critical topic. What will we always do? What will we never do? Mutual respect for team members – including our patients – is emphasized. We should disagree agreeably. Everyone should have everyone else's back. All work should be evenly shared among the residents, and the patients are the team's patients. This means that everyone must know the details of every patient on the team, in case the intern primarily responsible for a patient is off the floor. Knowing the clinical details of all patients encourages everyone to contribute ideas on how best to manage each patient.

7. **Decisions** are made by consensus. If there is a disagree-ment, then the attending has the last say, because they are ultimately legally responsible for each patient.

8. Finally, the **advantages of the system** are emphasized: shortened duration of rounds, shorter length of stay for patients, and shorter times required for the house staff to complete their daily work.

Study

To monitor how well the attending physician adhered to the rounding system, the case manager graded each attending using a five-point grading scale (1 = worst, 5 = best). The 30-point scale had six categories:

1. Facilitation of communication among team members.
2. Encouragement of problem-solving on rounds.
3. Encouragement of nurses and the case manager to participate in rounds.
4. Adherence to a rounding schedule.
5. Encouragement of work-sharing among team members.
6. Knowledge of key clinical details prior to rounds.

Performance thresholds were established for each category. Finally, anonymous surveys were conducted of both the control and experimental teams.

We plotted the duration of rounds for each day (Figure 6-3). For the AIR experimental teams, the duration of rounds steadily decreased as the teams improved their rounding fundamentals. By the second week, times were consistently below 120 minutes. The control rounding group, however, showed no improvement in the duration of rounds, reaching highs of 180 minutes on two occasions.

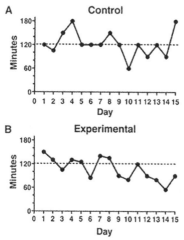

Figure 6-3. Daily rounds duration: control vs. experimental (AIR).

The AIR rounding system was also associated with significant improvements in reported job satisfaction of the attending physicians, residents, students, and nurses. The nurses on the floor where AIR was primarily conducted felt the physicians following the AIR protocol were more available, more likely to address their patient's needs, and more likely to be respectful. Improved nursing job satisfaction was important because improved satisfaction might reduce nursing turnover (typically 18 to 22% in the US) and reduce the high cost of replacing nurses (approximately $50,000 per nurse).

Finally, length-of-stay was shortened by 25% as compared to the other medical teaching services, and 30-day readmissions to the hospital, which are considered a failure in discharge planning, decreased from 22% to 7%.

If these performance measures were achieved throughout the system, we calculated that the teaching services responsible for managing 100 patients per day could free up 30 to 40 beds or increase their productivity by 30 to 40%, markedly increasing the number of patients we could care for each day. Full implementation of AIR could eliminate long Emergency Department waiting periods for an inpatient bed and would increase the hospital's capacity to accept referrals for specialized care from surrounding regions of the state.

Adjust: Leveraging Findings

Application of the skills and knowledge from the ALI program led to a successful implementation of adaptive change, and we shared our findings in the journal *Academic Medicine* (23). I was proud to call myself an adaptive leader, and I couldn't wait to apply these skills to other quality improvement projects. I felt like the sky was the limit.

However, I failed to realize that not everyone in the Department of Medicine beehive was working to accumulate honey . . .

Chapter 7: Becoming a Martyr

The scholar does not consider gold and jade to be precious treasures, but loyalty and good faith.
—Confucius

After a breath of fresh AIR, and soon after completing the leadership training fellowship at Harvard, a senior physician began complaining that my improvement efforts had 'distracted' me from my primary role as division chief. When I learned that he planned to meet with our Chair, I regretted that I had not listened to the many faculty who had warned me to dismiss him on my arrival as the new division chief. Allowing him to stay had reaped positive dividends (he published ground-breaking research), yet I was deeply disappointed that he used his new stature to undermine my leadership.

While the Chair of Medicine supported my efforts, he retired only three months later. Without his protection, I sensed danger. Complaining continued among others on staff. I had challenged the status quo, and now I was about to become a martyr.

Yet these events were outside my control. I voluntarily resigned as Infectious Diseases Division Chief and, not wanting our efforts to go up in flames, I embraced a new appointment as Quality Improvement Project Manager for our Health System with enthusiasm and humility.

Other personnel changes followed, and I moved my laboratory half a mile away to a new research building and withdrew from all infectious diseases conferences and meetings. Over the next year the newly appointed Chair of Medicine moved the division out of the Academic Research building, and away from our basic science collaborators to the Dental Tower, where the offices and labs were scattered among the dental school's clinics.

The infectious disease faculty felt like they had been moved to the Gulag, far away from other investigators and far away from the hospital wards. The division was offered minimal laboratory space and, most depressingly, the laboratories and offices had no windows. Faculty felt like they were working in a submarine. These conditions were the antithesis of the Thorndike Laboratories in Boston, conditions I had tried to emulate as division chief.

My First Assignment as Quality Improvement Project Manager

Soon after my new appointment I was assigned my first project: reducing post-operative infections in patients undergoing elective neurosurgery. This project was ideal because it utilized my thirty years of infectious disease expertise and newly acquired adaptive leadership skills. Five years earlier, an infection control challenge arose that was directly relevant to this new project.

During the 2005 season, 13 players on the university football team were sidelined because of serious methicillin-resistant *Staphylococcus aureus* (MRSA) infections. Then, at the start of the 2006 season, several players experienced MRSA skin infections. The head of the training staff contacted the Infectious Diseases Division for help. The 2005 outbreak had caused unnecessary absences and in 2006, the football team was ranked in the top 10 nationally. They were in the hunt for the national championship, and they could not afford another outbreak of MRSA.

The hospital epidemiologist, an infection control practitioner, and I arrived at the football training facility the next day. We were all highly motivated to determine the underlying causes of the football team's MRSA outbreak. We first designed a questionnaire that asked about past skin infections, exposure to others with skin infections, presence of cuts or scrapes, and sharing of equipment and toiletries as well as age and class year. We discovered three major risk factors that greatly increased the likelihood a player would contract an MRSA infection: a history of skin infections, contact with someone outside of the college with a skin lesion, and being a freshman or college transfer.

Sanitary interventions were immediately put in place. These interventions reduced the MRSA nasal carriage rate (the proportion of individuals in a population who have detectable bacteria in their nasal passages despite having no symptoms) from 31 out of 147 players in 2005 to 2 out of 140 in 2006 – and only two players experienced a significant MRSA infection. (24)

And the university won the NCAA National Football Championship that year!

A Very Painful Bee Sting

With this new experience under our belts, a team was assembled to reduce postoperative elective neurosurgery infections to zero. This project was potentially far more important than winning an NCAA Football Championship. If we succeeded, we could make a major difference in our patients' lives.

As we assembled for our first meeting, I planned to begin with a team launch as I had been taught at Harvard Business School. We would introduce ourselves, discuss our goals, discuss how we would communicate, and clarify our individual roles. We would make an estimate of the time frame for the completion of our task and then discuss behavior norms: what would we always do, and what we would we never do?

The neurosurgeon arrived five minutes late, wearing a well-tailored suit, a bright silk tie, and a tab-collared shirt with cufflinks and acting as if he were royalty. "We have already completed a pilot program," the neurosurgeon proudly stated. "During the study period we enrolled 125 patients, and not a single one had an infection, while there were six infections in the 800 patients who did not receive decontamination."

There were problems with this interpretation. Statistical analysis revealed that this difference could simply represent a chance variation. And yet this doctor was suggesting his intervention *had* made a difference. The most problematic issue was that he implemented his decontamination procedures **after** surgery. It was already well-established at the time that effective programs decontaminate surgical patients **before** surgery, to prevent the knife blade from introducing skin bacteria into the fresh surgical incision. Based on my understanding of decontamination and statistics, his efforts had been a waste of time.

Instead, he now wanted to utilize a rapid identification test using the polymerase chain reaction (PCR) to identify patients who were Staph carriers. They had a five-times greater chance of suffering from a postoperative infection than non-carriers. In our discussion, I emphasized that the key to preventing such infections was to decontaminate carriers **before** surgery.

As we reviewed possible scenarios for how to accomplish this task, we realized that PCR would ideally have a turnaround time of approximately twelve hours. However, by that time the patients would have left the clinic and would be staying in a hotel, waiting for their surgery. How would we contact them? How would we arrange to have the nasal antibiotic and anti-bacterial soap delivered to them prior to surgery? Furthermore, we would be using a $50 test to decide whether to employ a $45 decontamination treatment!

To further complicate the situation, anyone identified as a *Staphylococcus* carrier must be placed in a special isolation room and all hospital personnel who enter their room would be required to wear gowns and gloves. We subsequently learned that because these PCR tests were batched, the turnaround time was 24 hours rather than twelve hours, which meant in most cases *Staphylococcus* carriage would not be verified until after surgery.

What if we decontaminated all elective surgical patients 48 hours before surgery? This seemed to be a far simpler plan. We could eliminate the cost of PCR, the logistics of delivering the antibiotic cream and anti-bacterial soap to positive patients, and all patients would benefit from the antibacterial soap because everyone's skin contained significant concentrations of bacteria. Only one out of ten would truly benefit from the antibiotic nasal ointment; however, studies had shown that treatment for five days would do no harm. With this short decontamination protocol, there was minimal risk of increasing the selection of antibiotic-resistant Staphylococcus organisms.

Two weeks after our first meeting, I proposed this possibility in an email to the neurosurgeon and was met with name-calling – a never event in effective team communication. (Talk about a stinging bee. This guy was stinging wasp!) I replied factually: "My approach is based on my readings about the Toyota Production System as well as my experience decontaminating the football team."

Soon after this, a nurse reported that many of the residents were now ordering nasal antibiotics for all neurosurgery patients and maintaining their use for the entire time patients were hospitalized. Research indicated that if this practice continued antibiotic-resistant bacteria were highly likely to begin populating the Neurosurgery Intensive Care Unit (ICU).

In our next meeting, one month after our kickoff, I attempted to introduce some humor about this new development. The neurosurgeon stormed out of the room stating, "This project is over. I cannot work with this team." We sat in disbelief. Perhaps I should have avoided humor, as I had inadvertently stirred the bee's nest.

Silos in the Hive

As part of my new position, I also attempted to introduce information about organizing people to bring about cultural change. The encounter with neurosurgery emphasized the continued territoriality of our departments – they were often not aligned in their goals or definitions of 'honey'. Our system was not one integrated bee-hive, but rather a collection of beehives, all with different goals.

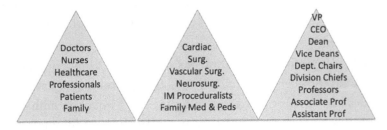

Figure 7-1. The three hierarchies of healthcare systems.

Furthermore, there were and continue to be multiple hierarchies within our medical center and all academic medical centers. The first hierarchy consists of the different healthcare professionals, with physicians being at the top followed by nurses and then other healthcare professionals with patients and families at the bottom (Figure 7-1).

The second hierarchy is exclusively related to physicians. Neu-rosurgeons, cardiovascular surgeons, and vascular surgeons are at the top of this pyramid followed by internal medicine procedural specialists (cardiology, pulmonary, gastroenterology), with primary care physicians in internal medicine, family medicine, and pediatrics being at the bottom. I had very recently experienced this hierarchy.

The third formal hierarchy consists of administrators. The Vice President for Health Affairs has ultimate power over everyone in the health center and the CEO of the health system is very near the top of this pyramid. Just below these two head administrators are the deans and vice deans, followed by the department chairs, division chiefs, tenured professors, clinical professors, associate pro-fessors, and assistant professors.

Given the multiple hierarchies and top-down leadership model, how could our health system emulate the ground-up leadership sys-tem practiced in beehives? The honeybee system makes decisions on the front lines through consensus on where to harvest nectar and pollen and where to place new nests. There is no supervisor mandating their actions.

To emulate this highly coordinated honeybee system, health systems needed to practice distributive leadership. Administrators need to recognize that leadership does not require a formal administrative title. Every healthcare professional on the front lines should be empowered to recognize their sphere of influence and lead.

Based on these recommendations, a healthcare leader should be defined as *anyone who influences others to objectively improve human health.*

A Ray of Light

One success I had as the Quality Improvement Project Manager at our healthcare system was the 'I Promise' campaign (Figure 7-2.). Begun while I was away on sabbatical, this program enlisted everyone who worked in the hospital to make a promise about how they as an individual could improve the quality and safety of patient care in our hospital. The goal of the campaign was to encourage all health professionals to lead improvements in how we care for patients.

Could I leverage this campaign theme to begin to change our culture, flatten our hierarchies and encourage distributive leadership?

First, I conducted one-on-one meetings with faculty who were trying to lead changes in their departments, scheduling a 30-minute coffee break with each candidate. At the end of each meeting, I asked if they would be willing to join our 'I Promise' campaign and become part of our leadership team. Fortunately, they all said yes!

Together we decided that our overall campaign theme should be communication. Then someone suggested, "Why not hold a hospital-wide forum where patients, doctors, nurses, and others can openly discuss the state of doctor-patient communication and suggest ways to improve communication?" We called our gathering the *Forum on Doctor-Patient Communication* (Figure 7-2).

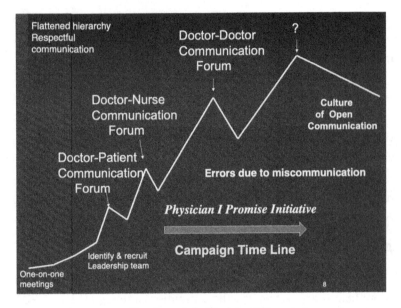

Figure 7-2. Timeline of the Physician 'I Promise' campaign.

Because our forum was an official hospital event, we were able to request support from the Public Affairs Office. They created posters and announced the Doctor-Patient Communication Forum in the hospital news magazine. They also provided pizza and salad for our meeting. As the clock struck 5:00, we worried; was anyone going to come? They did, and we attracted more than 75 participants from nearly every department in the hospital.

We began our program with two patients who each presented a five-minute 'Story of Self'. Our first patient had a genetic disorder. She bemoaned the fact that **there was "no one healthcare professional designated to organize and coordinate" her care.** The second patient was an Emergency Room (ER) physician who developed appendicitis. He came to the ER he worked in and was told he had gastroenteritis only to return six hours later in shock. He emphasized that when it comes to doctor-patient communication ,**"One small word and one small deed can make all the difference."**

Then the audience jumped in. They wanted to share their experiences. They wanted to propose solutions. The energy and goodwill in the room were palpable. There was no hierarchy that day. Everyone felt empowered to speak and everyone in the audience listened intently. The meeting flew by, lasting over an hour, and many thoughtful suggestions for improvement were offered.

Our campaign brought our committee and the forum participants together to focus on a common goal. We were off and running. A follow-up summary of our discussion was sent to all the participants. The intention at that time was to create a doctor-patient communication training program. During our forum, we shared not only the problems, but also potential solutions:

Listen:

- The number one request by patients was for the physician to truly listen.

- Listen to those with chronic illnesses, because they know their bodies and their illnesses. They know what doesn't work and what does.

- Patients often have insights into their pain thresholds that can be helpful in assessing their illness.

- Listening can save time and prevent errors.

- Listening is an important skill. There are four types of listening: informative, critical, empathic, and therapeutic. We all need to learn these specific listening skills to be on the same page.

- The approach to each patient will need to be different; different patients have different degrees of insight into their illnesses. We must understand where our patient is on this spectrum. The highly informed patient can be an asset if we can establish trust and understanding.

Build relationships with our patients:

- Patients often do not know the names of the physicians caring for them. It is important to let the patient know who the senior physician is. Patients want and need to know who is in charge.
- Patients want our respect and focus, and they want us to share our experience and our knowledge.
- Patients want to be treated just like a family member.
- Promote relationship centered patient care.
- Identify cues coming from our patients. Are they comprehending what we are saying?
- As physicians we need to know ourselves and understand our hidden biases.
- Humility is a wonderful trait that patients appreciate.
- Hold the reins gently and if you don't have the answer be honest and upfront.
- Physician faculty can serve as role models and by modeling a relationship-centered approach they can spread these behaviors to other caregivers including nurses, technicians, residents, and students.

Effectively manage the patient's illness:

- The message to the patient from multiple physicians needs to be consistent and aligned, or the patient will become distressed and fearful that no one knows what is going on.
- Common sense and practical approaches should be emphasized.
- Our understanding of each patient's disease must be accurate and thorough, or we lose trust. Beware of the danger of copying and pasting inaccurate information into our electronic records.

Improve patient satisfaction:

- Learn from best practices. The floor with the highest satisfaction survey ratings works as a team. Information is shared, and they pay attention to the little details. "They love their patients, and it shows."
- Patient satisfaction is multi-factorial and depends on all the systems of care functioning well.
- We need to be reliable and on time to build patient satisfaction.
- Spending excess time on the electronic record reduces our time with our patients and lowers satisfaction.
- As physicians, we have focused primarily on biomedical information. We will also need to focus on our interpersonal skills, on working in teams, and on understanding and improving our systems of care.

At the end of our forum, the hospital chaplain shared a quote from Saint Mother Teresa:

We can do no great things, we can only do little things with great love.

Subsequently, we held two additional very successful forums on doctor-nurse and doctor-doctor communication. Everyone was getting to know each other and to better understand the unique viewpoints of each group. And, once again, helpful suggestions for improvement were offered by the participants. By the completion of the third forum, we had recruited more than 250 participants, all of whom had provided their email contact, thus demonstrating a willingness to stay involved.

We were creating a new, far more collaborative culture with no significant hierarchy. We were rebuilding the honeybee colony. Nurses, patients, administrators, and physicians were on equal footing – just as observed among the thousands of worker bees servicing the beehive.

Colony Collapse

Unfortunately, our progress was abruptly halted because of the loss of my leg on September 18, 2012.

Disagreements about staff issues, and an unwillingness for any-one to take over my leadership role, ended our promising campaign. Soon thereafter, because of a *New York Times* Op-Ed (see chapter 2 – 'Upsetting the Bees'), I was removed from Projects Manager position and no longer had a position of power. I was subsequently suspended as a teaching attending. Without the ability to attend on the medical wards, I could no longer generate sufficient clinical revenue for my division.

On the medical wards, I was generally required to walk 4,000 to 5,000 steps – the maximum number I could tolerate without signif-icant residual limb pain. My suspension from this position would require me to generate revenue as an infectious disease consultant. However, this role often required faculty to walk over 10,000 steps per day because patients were distributed in multiple buildings sep-arated by long tunnels. The possibility of managing the physical demands of being a consultant was unrealistic.

And so, I was reassigned to the Division of Hospital Medicine where I served as the Admitting Officer of the Day (AOD), walking only short distances within the ER. As AOD I was able to use my extensive clinical experience to assist in deciding whether a patient should be admitted to the Internal Medicine service, referred to another service, or sent home. This enjoyable work required both diagnostic and interpersonal skills, although there were many road-blocks due to systems dysfunction as well as poor teamwork.

These experiences provided many new insights into the system challenges in health care. However, I was at the low point in my career: disabled, suspended from the medical teaching service, removed from my projects manager position, and removed from the Infectious Disease Division I had devoted 19 years to building.

As the beekeeper of an active hive, I had suffered multiple severe stings. In retrospect, the neurosurgeon was not receptive to 'outside interference.' Like a worker bee guarding the entrance of his hive against foreign bees, he was a highly competitive, top-down leader, and unwilling to collaborate. He did not acknowledge my expertise or experience, and my misguided attempt at humor backfired.

The 'I Promise' campaign was the only ray of sunshine during this highly stressful period. This campaign emphasized that, when presented with a positive forum, healthcare professionals *and* patients can find common ground. The success of this program proved that like honeybees, we can focus on what brings us together: providing the best possible care for our patients, our honey.

Chapter 8: Reexamining My Theory of Change

We need to discover the root causes of success rather than the root causes of failure.

—David Cooperrider

At the time of my appointment to the Division of Hospital Medicine, I realized I needed to reexamine my theory of change. Efforts to prevent postoperative neurosurgical infection did not take root, and emotional disequilibrium was created while trying to change work rounds in the Department of Medicine. Administrators reacted angrily when I publicly revealed that I lost my leg due to a medical error. Furthermore, the front-line efforts to bring about change were labor-intensive and becoming counterproductive.

The bottom line was that these efforts were unlikely to have a long-lasting impact.

Working Outside the Health System

Ironically, two of the founders of the patient safety movement, Dr. Don Berwick and Dr. Lucian Leape, had avoided direct efforts to bring about change in the institutions where they worked. This was because they understood that the steep and dense administrative hierarchies within medical centers stifled innovation. Instead, they brought about change by creating organizations outside of their local health systems: The Institute of Healthcare Improvement (IHI) and the National Patient Safety Foundation (NPSF).

These national organizations gave their founders free reign to innovate and teach, and the IHI and NPSF became the bedrock for healthcare quality improvement science. Physicians, nurses, administrators, and patients gathered under the umbrella of these organizations to create and share solutions. Through their annual meetings and white papers, they spread their knowledge nationally and internationally. These two organizations merged in 2017 and now all efforts are under the auspices of the Institute of Healthcare Improvement.

Scholarship

My own idea and the original project for my Advanced Leadership Initiative (ALI) Fellowship was to write a book describing how to improve the quality and safety of patient care. I envisioned a best-seller that would be widely read and have a national and worldwide impact. The primary audience would be nurses, a large constituency concerned with patient safety. Too often, when a patient suffered a preventable error, the nurse was blamed rather than the system. Nurses understand that improving the quality of patient care reduces the likelihood that they will be punished for systems errors out of their control. They would be less likely to select a red bead in Deming's Red Bead Experiment (chapter 6).

My 2012 book, *Critically Ill: A Five-point Plan to Cure Healthcare Delivery,* was based on my thirty years as a practicing physician, my courses at Harvard, and my extensive conversations with the Harvard faculty and ALI fellows. The conclusions of my book:

Everyone in health care needs to become a system thinker and attain the skills to transform our fragmented and dangerous health systems into highly integrated, efficient, and safe systems like those created by honeybees. This requires a deep understanding of the Toyota Production System (TPS) and the expertise to effectively apply the tools of TPS to bring about this system transformation.

Everyone should be skilled in creating and maintaining interdependent management teams that focus on the patient, flatten the hierarchy, and create psychological zones of safety to enable innovation and encourage effective problem-solving.

Everyone must understand the nature of human error and how to design systems that minimize error.

A distributive leadership model should be implemented whereby everyone becomes a leader and takes initiative for improvements in their sphere of influence. Adaptive leaders – leaders who can effectively lead change – should be developed and rewarded.

Healthcare professionals should apply the organizing methods used by renowned politicians to motivate others to embrace continual improvement within their health systems.

The book included many real patient cases that demonstrated the personal consequences of failing to make these changes, to touch the hearts of readers and open their minds to embrace the changes I recommended.

Teaching

Although many copies were sold, Critically Ill was not a best seller. Was there another way to spread the word and achieve a broader impact?

I began to explore Coursera, the most successful massive open online course (MOOC) platform used by millions of students and more than 200 university partners. My online Coursera course was entitled 'Fixing Healthcare Delivery'. This course covered the same material that was in the book using teaching videos and multiple-choice questions. On the first two-month run, the course attracted over 7,500 students including patients, nursing and medical students, healthcare professionals, and healthcare administrators. Over the past seven years, the course has remained active and has attracted over 30,000 students originating from 120 countries. The largest numbers of students have come from the US, Canada,

Europe, India, and Egypt.

To acquire the knowledge and training to teach a second course, I traveled to the Virginia Mason Institute for their three-month course 'Advanced Lean'. I then created another Coursera course, 'Fixing Healthcare Delivery 2.0: Advanced Lean.' This course provided a unique perspective from a physician working on the front lines, committed to preventing medical errors by continuously improving our care systems using TPS as a guide. This course is aimed at a narrower audience of healthcare professionals but has had over 4,900 students sign up since it launched in August of 2017.

I also used the instructional videos from these courses to teach our fourth-year medical students through a 'flipped classroom' format, whereby the student watches a set of videos the night before a face-to-face session with me as their instructor. Using a series of guiding questions, each student relates the content of the videos to their own personal experiences, and completes the course by applying their new knowledge and understanding to propose a quality improvement project that they can conduct during their residency. Over the past six years, more than 100 medical students have completed the course, and many continue to stay in touch.

Focus on the Positive: Appreciative Inquiry

To effectively teach these courses, I needed to continue to implement quality improvement projects on the front lines and share my successes and failures with my students. After my transfer to the Division of Hospital Medicine in 2015, in addition to serving as the Admitting Officer of the Day (AOD) in the Emergency Room, I was appointed the Director of Patient Care Quality and Safety for the Division.

Hospitalists face many operational issues and inefficiencies due to health system dysfunctions. My efforts at the medical center and department level had proved to be overly ambitious and destined to fail. This smaller playing field had far greater potential for meaningful and sustainable change.

We utilized an approach developed at Case Western Business School called 'Appreciative Inquiry'. A major problem with adaptive change is the sense of loss when old methods are discarded. Rather than focusing on what is to be eliminated, Appreciative Inquiry focuses on the current strengths of the organization and how they can be amplified. (25)

Our first goal was to improve teamwork between the hospital medicine and the emergency medicine faculty and residents. Our division was responsible for screening all Emergency Department (ED) admissions to Internal Medicine. Interactions would often turn negative because the ED faculty wanted a patient admitted and the internist AOD disagreed.

Recognizing that 'we are what we talk about', Appreciative Inquiry uses a positive vocabulary to create 'Positive Emotional Attractors' (PEAs). The use of strongly positive words stimulates the production of oxytocin and decreases the fight-and-flight hormones epinephrine and norepinephrine that impair effective communication. These conditions improve problem-solving and increase creative and innovative thinking. When discussing illness, the PEA 'wellness' is preferred over the word 'health', because wellness connotes a more positive image. Other PEAs include 'excellence' in place of 'effective,' 'extraordinary' rather than 'efficient,' and 'flawless' in place of 'reliable'.

Psychologists have found that it takes four positive statements to overcome the impact of one negative statement. Therefore, whenever possible, improvement needs to be framed in positive terms: as a challenge, as an opportunity to encourage a positive frame of mind and to inspire innovative change.

The 'Four-D Model' describes stages of the Appreciative Inquiry process:

1. **Discovery**: Appreciate what is good in the current system.
2. **Dream**: Imagine what the ideal state would look like.
3. **Design**: Create the processes required to achieve the ideal state.

4. **Destiny**: Empower everyone to continually learn and adapt to assure that the new system is sustained.

Another key activity in effective Appreciative Inquiry is to encourage all participants to share stories of their positive experiences. The human brain easily remembers and can be inspired by personal stories. This approach mirrors the use of personal narratives by politicians and other organizers to persuade and motivate others to support their cause. Unlike problem-solving sessions that usually rely on a few higher-level leaders, Appreciative Inquiry encourages all members to recall their personal experiences.

This approach highlights the role of frontline personnel in shaping the future. Their involvement in creating the vision means that proposed changes will be well-received. This is a 'bottom-up' decision-making process, just as seen in honeybee colonies. Appreciative Inquiry encourages distributive leadership, the form of leadership so badly needed in our health systems.

I held two meetings with the ED faculty, introducing them to our new, more positive, approach.

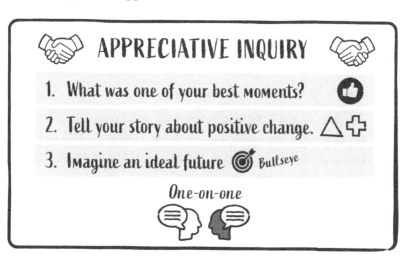

Figure 8-1. Three key questions to guide positive inquiry.

95

I first asked them, "When thinking about Emergency Room patient flow, please think back to a recent time that stands out as one of the good or best days or moments and tell me a short story about it." (Figure 8-1, question 1.)

After a member of the audience shared their story, I asked, "How do you remember feeling at that time? Why does it stand out as a high point to you today?"

Next, I asked the audience to share a story about positive change (Figure 8-1, question 2). "With regards to patient flow in the ER and/or hospital please recall a project that you would call a 'positive change'?"

Once a story was shared, I asked "What was it about you – your strengths – that helped make that story a success? What was it about the other(s) that helped make it a success? What other organizational or situational factors also helped make it a successful change effort?"

Finally, I asked each member of the audience to imagine an ideal future (Figure 8, question 3):

> Imagine it is two years from now. How are patients being managed in the ER and in the hospital? Everything is as you always wished it could be. You feel as though you are fulfilling a calling or higher purpose, rather than just earning a good paycheck.
>
> What do you see? How have others around you changed? What hurdles did you overcome to get to this ideal situation? Please share whatever words, thoughts or descriptions come to mind.

After sharing their answers to these questions, the ED faculty were inspired and expressed a strong desire to work with the Hospital Medicine faculty to achieve an ideal future. We were off and running!

Over the next three months, we instituted a standardized hand-off that described the severity of the patient's illness, pertinent patient historical details, action items, and contingency plans. The listener in the hand-off was then asked to summarize what they had heard, and the presenter corrected any inaccuracies.

These changes improved both patient flow and teamwork. Faculty from both departments had developed a shared vision and worked as an interdependent team. Disparaging comments were no longer common and job satisfaction in the ED improved markedly.

Appreciative Inquiry had allowed us to make meaningful adaptive changes without creating emotional disequilibrium. By encouraging the faculty to create a shared vision, everyone owned the improvements and had an emotional stake in the project's success. Our goals were aligned, and we had become very much like worker honeybees focused on producing sufficient honey to survive. We had become members of the same beehive.

Plan: Building on Success

We used this same approach to design an efficient bedside rounding program that focused on effective and efficient communication with each patient and their bedside nurse. During the Hospital Medicine retreat, we asked the following question with the goal of improving patient-centered care: "Can you tell me a time when you or your team went the extra mile to care for patients, a time you recall feeling proud, energized, engaged, and fulfilled from being a part of a change or improvement that was meaningful to you and others? Tell a story about that experience."

We conducted follow-up questions using the same format we used with the ED faculty.

Using these narratives, and keeping in mind our recently published survey of patients who had suffered harm due to medical errors (see chapter 3 – 'A Broader View'), as well as our previous Doctor-Patient Communication Forum, we identified two major goals: 1) involve our patients in decision making, and 2) assure care was coordinated with the bedside nurse by creating a standardized bedside communication tool.

To create this communication tool, we incorporated the conclusions of a large multidisciplinary committee consisting of nurses, physicians, patients, and administrators, who had determined all the key conditions required to maximize patient satisfaction. We compiled a list of eleven separate components and initially used a paper checklist to ensure that all eleven elements were covered on rounds; however, this proved to be time-consuming and unwieldy.

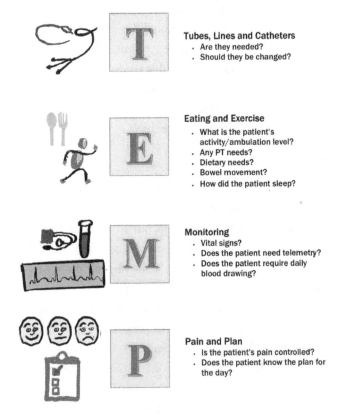

Figure 8-2. Bedside rounding TEMP checklist.

Instead of a paper checklist, we developed a mnemonic, TEMP, which categorized the eleven elements into four groups (Figure 8-2):

- **T** stands for **tubes**; central IV line and Foley catheter. Are they required? Can they be removed? Removal of an unnecessary foley or bladder catheter markedly reduces the risk of a catheter-associated urinary tract infection (CAUTI) and removal of a central intravenous line eliminates the risk of a central-line-associated bloodstream infection (CLABSI).

- **E** stands for **exercise**: How much activity is ordered for the patient? Patients on bedrest quickly become de-conditioned and too weak to return home, necessitating placement in an inpatient rehabilitation facility. **E** also stands for **eating** and encourages the nurse and physician to review the patient's diet to assure they are receiving sufficient calories and nutrients. **E** includes **excretion**. When did the patient last have a bowel movement? Sleep also naturally falls into this category because irregular sleep slows healing and can lead to delirium, delaying discharge. Blood draws and vital signs can be avoided during sleep to reduce the risk of these complications.

- **M** stands for **monitoring**: Does the patient still require telemetry (cardiac monitoring)? Too often, patients are left on a cardiac monitor despite the absence of arrhythmia or irregular heartbeats. Telemetry is labor-intensive, requiring visual monitoring by a technician and discontinuation allows technicians to pay closer attention to patients with arrhythmias. **M** also stands for **monitoring of vital signs**. On admission, blood pressure, pulse, respiratory rate, and temperature are usually measured every four hours; however, once the patient has stabilized, these measurements can be taken every eight hours reducing nursing labor. The final monitoring category is **blood tests**. These are often unnecessarily ordered on a daily basis despite stable results. These monitoring tests can often be reduced to every other day,

- saving blood and labor, and allowing the patient to experience a day without being stuck with needles.

- **P** stands for **pain control**: is the patient's pain being
  controlled to a level of six out of ten or lower? Discussions between the patient, nurse, and physician allow more
  effective pain management. Finally, **P** stands for the **daily
  plan of care**. The physician reviews the diagnostic tests and
  treatments planned for the day with the patient and nurse
  and explains the rationale for these plans. The patient and
  nurse are both encouraged to ask questions. At the end
  of the conversation, the physician conducts a 'teach-back',
  asking the patient if they understand the plan for the day
  and asking them to summarize it back to them so they can
  correct any misunderstandings (Figure 8-2).

Do

This seemingly long list usually took only one or two minutes to
cover and, combined with examining the patient and asking about
new symptoms, bedside rounds took an average of only six minutes
per patient. By covering this information face-to-face, the paging of
doctors by nurses was dramatically reduced and the patient's questions
were answered in a timely fashion. On occasion, the need for longer
patient conversations became clear, and the hospitalist arranged these
meetings after rounds so as not to take up the nurses' valuable time.

Initially, many of the hospitalists were reticent to apply the new
rounding system, and the Chief of the Division and I conducted a
weekly huddle to review what was going well and what could be
improved. During these sessions, the nurses expressed their appreciation and reported that the TEMP system reduced errors and
improved the care of their patients.

As a result, the nurses reported that they now understood the
plans for the day and no longer needed to page the physicians to
clarify the plans. Because the nurse was present while the physician was communicating with the patient, the nurse could often
answer questions about the plan for the day after the physician left

the room, thereby reducing the need for the patient and family to call the physician for clarifications.

Study

In addition to our weekly huddle, we recruited graduate students to monitor each physician's adherence to the rounding protocol.

A specific score was given for each element of the mnemonic that was covered, and a point was given if the bedside nurse was present during rounds. Prior to the formal training of the nurses and physicians, adherence averaged 35%. During the first phase of the trial, nurses and physicians were trained, and huddles were conducted resulting in adherence increasing to 60%. In the second phase of the trial, adherence scores were shared during rounds and emailed to each physician daily. Average adherence increased to 70–75%. (26)

Several outcome measures markedly improved after these interventions. The length of stay decreased by 25 hours after the second intervention, and the reduction in the length of stay closely correlated with the level of adherence. When adherence was only 35%, the average length of stay was comparable to pre-intervention, about 110 hours. However, when adherence reached 70%, length of stay dropped to 85 hours. (27)

This finding represented a critical take-home lesson: training alone had only a modest impact on adherence to the protocol and improvement in outcome measures. **Monitoring and feedback were critical to achieve faithful adherence to the protocol** and to achieve meaningful improvements in outcomes.

Another exciting outcome: the application of TEMP eliminated *all* catheter-associated bladder infections and *all* central line infections. (27) Catheter-associated bladder infections on average increase the cost of care by over $50,000 and increase the need to be placed in an intensive care unit (ICU). Central line infections have been shown to increase the cost of care by $25,000 per episode and are associated with mortality rates as high as 35%.

Eliminating these hospital-acquired infections was a major

accomplishment.

Lastly, we also observed a dramatic reduction in the patient readmission rate, from 22% to 11%.

Adjust

These very positive outcomes were described in two excellent clinical papers and represent the most successful improvement project of my career. (26, 27) With the strong leadership of the Chief of Hospital Medicine and the application of Appreciative Inquiry, we made remarkable progress. Both programs had been effectively implemented. Our projects illustrated the impressive positive impacts of effective communication.

Communication: What the Bees Know

While our progress felt hugely positive, as noted in chapter 1, honeybees had achieved this same goal millions of years earlier, emphasizing the universal importance of communication.

Worker bees often fly several miles from the hive looking for flowering plants that contain large supplies of nectar. When they discover a rich source, upon returning to the hive, they communicate the direction and distance of the site through a brief 'waggle dance', which is observed by the other worker bees huddled around the dancing bee. The angle of the tail relays the direction, and the duration of the dance relays the distance; the longer the dance, the greater the distance. When multiple returning bees perform the same waggle dance, it indicates a richer nectar supply and more bees are encouraged to visit the site and transport nectar back to the hive. (2)

Effective communication within the colony reduces the unnecessary expenditure of energy searching for new sources of nectar and pollen. The worker bees share their experiences and coordinate their efforts to maximize efficiency. Healthcare professionals can attain similar coordination and efficiency by using standardized communication tools, thereby substantially reducing preventable medical errors.

Communicating Progress Using a Visual Control

A very helpful tool that TPS uses to monitor the progress of its manufacturing processes is visual control.

If an assembly line is moving too slowly, a yellow light warns of the slowdown. This alerts a team of experts to quickly swarm the area where the slowdown has occurred, investigate the cause, and correct the condition that is leading to the delay. This visual control ensures the timely production of each automobile by eliminating delays and optimizing manufacturing efficiency.

Could we create a visual control that signaled a slowdown in the progress of patient care?

I found the ideal visual control upon reviewing operating procedures at a UK National Health Service (NHS) hospital called the 'Red Flag'. Each time a patient procedure or service was delayed, a Red Flag alert was placed on the electronic chart notifying administrators of a delay and the project administrator problem-solved to remove the impediment to efficient patient care.

This led to our Red Flag study, which began in June 2015, and was completed in June 2022. In the study, we compared performance measures during this period to the performance measures for the same medical wards for the 1 year prior to the start of the Red Flag initiative (from June 2014 to May of 2015). During the study period, the physician could add a Red Flag alert on a patient's electronic record, indicating a delay of over 24 hours in completing a subspecialty consultation, an imaging study (examples: an MRI or cardiac ultrasound), an invasive procedure (examples: upper gastrointestinal tract endoscopy or pulmonary bronchoscopy), or a delay in patient referral to a skilled nursing facility (SNF), inpatient rehabilitation, or long-term acute care facility (LTAC).

The Red Flag project also encouraged physicians to continually reexamine the need for hospitalization. If the physician could answer the question, "Does my patient need to be in the hospital?" with a "No," then the patient could be discharged from the hospital with close outpatient follow-up or be referred to an LTAC or SNF.

The red flags were monitored daily at 10 a.m. by an administrator who immediately contacted the responsible service and asked how their service could be facilitated. By troubleshooting, the administration was able to overcome many hospital roadblocks.

Following these interventions, the length of stay of patients steadily decreased. In the year prior to implementation of the Red Flag Day visual control, the average length of stay was 1.20, meaning the actual length of stay was 1.2 x longer than expected for the patient's illness. Within the first year, this value decreased to 1.15, then to 1.11 in Years Two and Three, 1.05 in Year Four, 1.02 in Year Five, and 1.0 in Year Six.

Over the period of Red Flag implementation, we reduced the length of stay by 20%, allowing us to care for more patients with the same number of physicians, nurses, and hospital beds.

Success

By 2019, after applying Appreciative Inquiry to implement the TEMP bedside checklist and the Red Flag notification system, the conditions for bringing about change and improving the quality and efficiency of patient care were ideal. Everyone in the division was aligned and embraced continual improvement. Teamwork and communication between our nurses and physicians were highly effective. The morale of the division was high, and job satisfaction among our faculty was the highest of any division in the Department of Medicine.

Furthermore, objective performance measures showed that our faculty were steadily improving, and our improvements were sustained. With the strong support of my division chief and the positive can-do attitude of our faculty, we acquired the Holy Grail: sustainable improvement combined with a culture that embraced teamwork and innovation. Our highly efficient system truly emulated that of a honeybee colony. Little did I know that our culture and operating systems were about to be severely tested.

Chapter 9: Overcoming the Challenges of the COVID-19 Pandemic

A great plague to you yourself and to men . . . shall be.
  —Zeus

Figure 9-1. Drawing of Pandora's Jar Spewing Out Deadly Coronavirus. (artwork by Bruno Lucchesi commsioned and purchased by F. Southwick]

According to myth, when angered by the deceptions of the human Prometheus, Zeus gave the curious maiden, Pandora, a jar that she couldn't help but open, releasing pestilence throughout the world (Figure 9-1).

A real-time pandemic reared its ugly head in January 2020. The mysterious acute respiratory illness emerged in a live animal market in Wuhan China. The virus was quickly sequenced and identified as a coronavirus closely related to SARS-CoV-1 and named SARS-CoV-2. Symptomatic SARS-CoV-2 infection was later called COVID-19 to avoid any geographic references or stigma.

SARS-CoV-1, like its new relative, originated in China and was first identified in the winter of 2002. The virus quickly spread to Hong Kong via a highly infectious business traveler, who spread the virus in a large hotel. By March 2003, significant numbers of cases had been discovered in Singapore, Taiwan, Vietnam, the US, and Canada.

As many readers can probably recall, the clinical presentation of SARS CoV-1 was worrisome. Most cases were in previously healthy adults aged 25 to 70. The illness began with high fever, often accompanied by severe shaking chills. Other common complaints included headaches, muscle aches, and generalized weakness. Early in the course of illness, some patients experienced mild respiratory symptoms and significant numbers had diarrhea. This was followed by more ominous symptoms: a dry cough accompanied by shortness of breath and low arterial oxygen levels (hypoxia). Chest X-rays revealed widespread pneumonia and ten to twenty percent of patients required ventilator support.

We had no effective anti-viral agent and corticosteroids were found to be of no benefit. The only treatment was supportive care. (28) The mortality exceeded 9%. Infectious disease experts throughout the world were extremely worried. Could this virus cause a repeat of the devastating 1918-1919 Influenza pandemic? It had resulted in 500 million infections and 50 million deaths worldwide.

In December 2003, SARS-CoV-1 disappeared. Worldwide, 8,098 cases were identified in 29 countries resulting in 774 deaths.

In the US, no one died from SARS-CoV-1. I breathed a deep sigh of relief. At the beginning of the outbreak, I had envisioned our intensive care units (ICUs) being overrun with patients suffering severe SARS-CoV-1 pneumonia. We were fortunate to have encountered a deadly virus that spread *inefficiently* from person to person. Quick action by the World Health Organization (WHO) and the Centers for Disease Control (CDC) contained the epidemic, and we didn't encounter a single case of SARS-CoV-1 in the counties surrounding our hospital.

I realized we had dodged a bullet, but I wondered about a future outbreak with a similarly deadly coronavirus that was more contagious. Reading reports about SARS-CoV-2 in January 2020, I feared my earlier concern was justified. The attack rates for this newly discovered virus were very high (i.e., a high percentage of the population was becoming infected) indicating that this coronavirus was highly contagious. Our medical center, and those worldwide, would not be spared this time.

I feared a future of surges of severely ill patients filling our ICUs and overwhelming our healthcare systems.

Compared to SARS-CoV-1, patients infected with SARS-CoV-2 usually had no symptoms early in the infection; however, during this asymptomatic period, they could shed high concentrations of virus from their respiratory tract, infecting others. In South Korea, one middle-aged woman spread the virus to 1,160 people while attending a megachurch and eating at a restaurant. We now realized that some asymptomatic infected patients were 'super-spreaders'.

As the infectious disease expert in our division, I was charged with reviewing the latest data on SARS-CoV-2. To effectively disseminate my findings and to counter the large volumes of disinformation being spread on the internet, I again turned to the Coursera platform to create a massive open online course (MOOC) for the layperson entitled 'COVID-19: A Clinical Update'. With my extensive experience creating educational videos for the two quality improvement Coursera courses I had previously produced, I was able to create the course in less than one month. It was first published in early April 2020 and quickly attracted students from all parts of the world, totaling 23,000 as of April 2023.

The massive surge in hospitalizations continued worldwide and resulted in severe shortages of face masks, gowns, gloves, and mechanical ventilators, and overwhelmed hospital personnel. The CDC's Morbidity and Mortality Weekly Report (MMWR) of November 20, 2020, noted that the high mortality rate for hospitalized patients in New York City (30%) raised concerns "that healthcare system capacity constraints might have influenced patient outcomes."

Death rates for COVID-19 steeply increased with age, being 0.9% for ages 18-44, 5.7% for ages 45-64, 18.4% for ages 65-74, and 38.3% for those 75 years or older.

I had just turned 75 years old, which meant that if I contracted COVID-19, my chances of dying were one in 2.6. Great odds for a horse race, but close to a death sentence when it came to COVID-19. In New York City, mortuaries were overwhelmed and refrigerated trucks were required to house the overflow of bodies.

Nurses and doctors were working excessive hours, risking their lives, and potentially risking the lives of their families to meet the overwhelming health needs of these critically ill patients. A recent study of US physicians revealed that from March 2020 through December 2021, 622 physicians died from COVID-19 (43/100,000). (29) Reports of physician fatalities served as a warning that all caregivers needed to be exceedingly careful in managing their personal protective equipment (PPE). Impeccable infection control practices were paramount.

As I reviewed these statistics, I felt like I was waiting for a tsunami to hit the Southeast. When would the tidal wave of cases hit, and would we suffer the same fate as NYC? Physicians over 65 years of age in our health system were asked to work from home and a telemedicine program was created that allowed physicians to care for patients virtually.

By mid-March 2020 our hospital laboratory had developed the molecular RT-PCR test for the virus. But because of limited supplies, tests were reserved for those who had symptoms suggestive of COVID-19 and were being considered for hospital admission. Coincident with the availability of the molecular test for SARS-CoV-2, we began to admit SARS-CoV-2 infected patients.

Because the virus was highly infectious and potentially deadly, trainees including medical students and residents were not permitted to admit or care for SARS-CoV-2 patients except for patients requiring ICU treatment. All SARS-CoV-2-positive patients were assigned to the Hospital Medicine faculty. This meant that our division would be experiencing the full impact of the coming surges of COVID-19 patients.

How did our division respond to this grave challenge? Our division chief began holding weekly town hall meetings to review our staffing allocations and to discuss up-to-date management plans.

First Controversy

We faced two management controversies early in the pandemic. The first controversy was the use of the anti-malaria drug hydroxychloroquine. The current literature claimed that the drug was effective for the treatment of COVID-19, yet the research designs were seriously flawed, the number of cases small, and the conclusions biased. Furthermore, hydroxychloroquine's primary mode of action is alkalinizing intracellular vacuoles or small compartments within macrophages and other host cells. This change in vacuole pH interferes with malaria replication but would *not* be expected to affect viral replication. Also of concern, hydroxychloroquine affected the electrical conduction of the heart and could cause abnormal cardiac rhythms. To guard against this side effect, all patients receiving this drug were required to undergo periodic electrocardiograms, adding to the complexity of care.

Plan

Based on the poor clinical trial data, the drug's mechanism of action, and its potential toxicity, in February of 2020, I strongly recommended avoiding treatment with hydroxychloroquine. At that time, the Infectious Disease Society of America (IDSA) also recommended against administering this drug unless it was part of a clinical trial. My recommendations and those of the IDSA were in direct opposition to the hospital administration's recommendations.

Do

The outcome: patients unnecessarily received hydroxychloroquine during our first COVID-19 surge that continued from February thru June of 2020.

Study

In June 2020, the FDA cautioned against the use of hydroxychloroquine for the treatment of COVID-19. Subsequently, large randomized clinical trials (RCTs) proved definitively that hydroxychloroquine was of no benefit for prevention (30) or treatment of COVID-19. (31)

Adjust

Final resolution: this medication was discontinued at our hospital at the end of June 2020.

Second Controversy

Our second controversy surrounded the use of face masks. At our first town hall meeting, I reviewed how the virus replicated in host cells and emphasized its rapid growth rate, and how asymptomatic carriers with high concentrations of virus in their nasal passages could quickly spread the virus by simply breathing and talking. I therefore encouraged our faculty to always wear a mask in the hospital.

Plan

My recommendation contradicted the preliminary infection control measures of our administration, who recommended wearing face masks, eye protection, gowns, and gloves only when managing known SARS-CoV-2 infected patients. However, because masks were in short supply, the administration recommended that physicians not wear masks when treating other patients.

I objected, "What about asymptomatic patients? Shouldn't healthcare professionals wear masks at all times?"

The administration initially refused to change their policy, expressing the concern that if doctors and nurses wore masks for all patients, they would frighten uninfected patients and their families.

At several medical centers including the University of Iowa, physicians were wearing protective face shields normally worn by welders and other workers to protect their eyes and face. These shields could be easily cleaned and reused. Although not ideal, face shields could prevent respiratory droplets from reaching the mouth and nose.

Do

Preliminary resolution: I was able purchase 60 face shields on the internet, and we distributed face shields to all front-line hospitalists by March of 2020.

Study

Face shields were shown to reduce SARS-CoV-2 infections in healthcare workers in India. (32) Multiple studies have demonstrated that tight fitting masks (N-95 and K-95) effectively reduced persons-to-person spread of the virus. (33-35)

Adjust

Final resolution: After approximately one and a half months, the administration's policy was changed to universal masking and N-95 masks were supplied to all hospital personnel. All hospital visitors were asked to wear face masks at all times, except when eating or drinking.

After the reagents were widely available for molecular testing, the hospital changed its testing policy. All patients being considered for hospital admission underwent testing to identify all asymptomatic carriers.

Solution-Focused Town Hall Meetings

In our town hall meetings, we also discussed how to improve our treatment protocols. The first major improvement related to the management of severe COVID-19 pneumonia, and during this discussion we emphasized the importance of the early administration of nasal oxygen. In our next town hall meeting we discussed our second management improvement. A large, randomized control trial (RCT) from the UK's National Health Service (NHS) proved that corticosteroids reduced pulmonary inflammation and improved patient outcome. (36)

Solution: Our division added to our standardized care protocol the immediate administration of the corticosteroid dexamethasone to all COVID-19 pneumonia patients with reduced arterial oxygen levels.

In a subsequent town hall meeting we discussed our third management improvement. A robust National Institutes of Health (NIH) Adaptive COVID-19 Treatment Trial 1 (ACTT-1) RCT trial demonstrated that administration of the anti-viral drug remdesivir within five days of symptom onset reduced the need for mechanical ventilation and reduced mortality. (37) By blocking virus RNA synthesis this agent stopped the growth of the virus and halted disease progression.

Solution: We established that the standard of care for our service would be the administration of IV remdesivir within 12 hours of admission for all patients with symptomatic SARS-CoV-2 infection.

Understanding the importance of ordering the appropriate blood tests to assess the level of inflammation and organ function, as well as instituting timely treatment, we agreed to fully standardize how we cared for our COVID-19 patients.

Solution: We created a COVID-19 order set and a standardized prog-ress note template. These tools assured that every patient received the same baseline laboratory evaluation and initially received the most up-to-date treatment regimen.

During the first surge, I consulted (through our telemedicine portal) on more than 80 complicated cases on the Hospitalist Service that required additional management.

Two of those patients were particularly challenging and illus-trated how labor-intensive and stressful the management of COVID-19 patients can be.

Telemedicine Case One

The first patient was a middle age respiratory therapist from another healthcare institution. Six days before her hospital admis-sion she was changing tracheostomy tubes and cleaning trache-ostomy sites. She later discovered that three of her patients had positive RT-PCR tests for SARS-CoV-2.

Three days later, she was turned away from her diabetes clinic during screening because she was found to have a fever. Four days after exposure, she began experiencing fatigue, fever, chills, and a dry hacking cough. The next day, as she walked to the kitchen, she became very short of breath, and over the next 24 hours, her shortness of breath became progressively worse. Being a respiratory therapist, she checked her oxygen saturation; it was 83%, far below normal (94–100%). She was rushed to the ER. Her chest CT scan showed extensive opacifications or infiltrates in both lungs, indicat-ing severe wide-spread pneumonia.

Over the next 12 days, she remained on a respirator, and on hospi-tal day six, she received convalescent plasma (plasma from a patient who has recovered from COVID-19). Forty-eight hours later, her BP returned to normal, her renal function normalized, and her oxygenation improved. On the seventeenth day of hospitalization, she was taken off the respirator and subsequently required several months of physical therapy to regain her strength.

Telemedicine Case Two

The second patient was a middle-aged internal medicine physician who was performing consults for the psychiatry service, where he was exposed to several patients whose RT-PCR tests were found to be positive for SARS-CoV-2. Three days later, he developed a dry hacking cough, fever, and chills and noticed a decreased sense of smell and taste. These symptoms were rapidly followed by increasing shortness of breath. On arrival at the ER, his oxygen saturation was 85%.

His chest CT scan showed extensive infiltrates or opacifications in both lungs, indicating severe wide-spread pneumonia. He was immediately placed on nasal oxygen, which increased his oxygen saturation to 95%. He was given the remdesivir and intravenous dexamethasone.

Over the next three days, he required higher and higher levels of oxygen. After being placed on an oxygen rebreather mask delivering 100% oxygen, his respiratory rate increased to 35–40 breaths per minute. He was panicking and reported, "I feel like I am drowning."

Because his oxygen levels could not be maintained, he was intubated and placed on a mechanical ventilator. An intensivist ordered a paralyzing agent to prevent the patient from fighting the respirator and, following this treatment, his arterial oxygen levels markedly improved. Over the next ten days, he continued to require ventilator support. On the tenth day of mechanical ventilation, his endotracheal tube was removed, and he was placed on nasal oxygen.

He had come very close to dying. His wife and three children and our fellow physicians and nurses caring for him had followed his downward clinical course in horror. We were greatly relieved that he had survived. We knew from personal experience and the medical reports coming from China, Europe, and NYC, that many patients hospitalized with such severe COVID-19 were not so lucky.

Contingency Plans

In addition to discussing the latest findings about COVID-19 during our town hall meetings, our division chief outlined our staff allocation plans. When the number of COVID-19 patients exceeded 80 on our service, faculty agreed to volunteer to come in for extra shifts, to assure that no one physician had to manage an excessive number of cases.

Our contingency plans were effective for all four surges: the first surge from February thru April of 2020, resulted in a peak daily census of 120 patients; the second in Summer 2020, peaking at 110 patients; followed by the Summer and Fall 2021 peak of 130; and our final surge peaked at 87 cases per day in January through March 2022. For each surge, the productivity of our division matched demand.

Debrief: How We Succeeded

To manage the unpredictable challenges of the COVID-19 pandemic, we followed the principles of Highly Reliable Organizations (HROs) (38). This organizational structure is used in forest fire-fighting crews, aircraft carrier flight deck personnel, and operators of nuclear reactors.

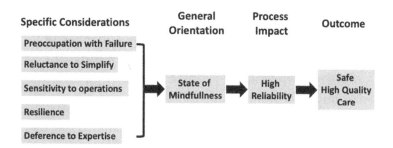

Figure 9-2. Principles of Highly Reliable Organizations (HRO).

There are five basic principles that all members of these organizations follow (Figure 9-2). Members of an HRO are:

1. Preoccupied with failure and anticipating what could go wrong

In our town hall meetings, we continually discussed potential challenges to patient care. By anticipating what could go wrong we were able to create contingencies.

For example, during the third COVID-19 surge caused by the delta variant, we observed that patients often rapidly progressed from severe to critical and could suddenly require intubation and mechanical ventilation. Such rapid deterioration required that the intensivist arrive within minutes to perform the intubation and to transfer the critically ill patients to the medical ICU. In anticipation of this potential problem, we arranged for the on-call intensivist to carry a special cell phone that hospitalists could call to assure their rapid arrival.

2. Reluctant to oversimplify

My periodic updates on COVID-19 meant that the faculty understood the complexity and evolving nature of up-to-date COVID-19 care. In addition, our division chief repeatedly described the complexities of the systems we were working within and explained how she was attempting to coordinate support within these systems.

3. Sensitive to system operations and continually mapping and assessing each system's function and empowering everyone to make suggestions for improvement

As Director of Patient Care Quality and Safety, I emphasized the importance of being a systems thinker, and during our town hall meetings, many faculty made helpful suggestions on how to improve our systems of care.

4. Committed to resilience

Everyone within the division expected failures and we frequently and quickly reviewed all failures, learned from our mistakes, and created improvements to prevent these mistakes from recurring. We had been conducting morbidity and mortality conferences monthly for the past five years. During these conferences, all faculty participated in root cause analysis and created plan-do-study-adjust cycles to correct any deficiencies. We saw deficiencies as opportunities, and the morale of our division was high because we knew that everyone had each other's back. In addition, our division chief went out of her way to remove any impediments to care and was always available for support and advice.

5. Deference to expertise

As hospitalists, we worked very closely with sub-specialist services and encouraged our faculty not to second-guess these experts. If we had differences of opinion everyone was encouraged to disagree agreeably. After our differences were aired, in nearly all cases, management decisions were made by consensus. All faculty respected and consistently followed the recommendations of our sub-specialists.

Our division chief carefully designed staffing contingency plans, thereby reducing faculty anxiety. Suggestions for improvement were encouraged by all faculty during our meetings. Many open and frank discussions resulted in suggestions for improving our systems of care.

Lessons from Bees about Shared Decision Making

The selection of sites for new nesting sites is a major event in the life of a bee colony that requires bottom-up decisions and careful orchestration. In early summer, several daughter queens mature, and the mother queen is then forced to leave the nest and start a new beehive. She is accompanied by about 10,000 worker bees.

Prior to this mass exodus, a group of older forager worker bees take on the role of scout bees assigned to hunt for a new dwelling

117

site. These bees share a common goal of choosing the nesting site that will maximize their chances of surviving the first winter.

The scouts declare their favorite sites using the waggle dance. Initially, scouts declare different sites as their favorite, but over three or four days, increasing numbers favor one site until eventually the scouts come to a consensus by all performing the same waggle dance. Following their decision, the queen and swarm travel to and take up residence in the chosen location.

Their behavior is comparable to the town hall meetings we created to address the SARS-CoV-2 surges. Just like scout bees, at the meetings, faculty initially proposed different solutions and then came to a consensus. The participation of many faculty generated a rich collection of solutions far superior to those that could be created by a single individual. Decisions were made in town hall meetings using bottom-up problem-solving, like foraging and scout honeybees. This democratic approach has allowed honeybees to survive for over 100 million years and enabled us to overcome the multiple COVID-19 surges.

Thanks to our division's town hall meetings, everyone understood the rationale for all decisions, how our systems for delivery had been designed, and followed our mutually agreed upon protocols. This understanding and the ability to make suggestions provided the faculty with a sense of control.

We combined all the ingredients required to create a resilient organization. Strong social support by the faculty and administration, combined with a strong sense of control encouraged a positive attitude and active coping. During the four COVID-19 surges, not a single faculty member required time off because of burnout, and only one faculty member required brief hospitalization for COVID-19.

A Successful Case Series: Treatment of COVID-19 in India

In addition to telemedicine consults at our medical center, in collaboration with a fellow faculty member and infectious diseases specialist who originally trained in India, we conducted daily 'Zoom Infectious Diseases Rounds' for a satellite hospital in rural India. This temporary hospital was specifically opened to manage COVID-19 cases during the massive surge of delta variant cases. Rounds were conducted daily for one hour, from May thru July of 2021.

This new rural hospital was run by a very thoughtful and collaborative internist who supervised four internal medicine residents. The residents presented each case to us, and together we estimated illness severity, prognosis, the need for additional tests, and the most appropriate therapy. The hospital managed approximately ten patients per day and treated a total of 83 patients.

We applied the same standardized approach used on our Hospital Medicine service. Each patient received a set of blood tests to determine the severity of inflammation, a chest CT scan, as well as oxygen saturation, blood pressure and heart rate measured every four hours. Based on the level of inflammation, severity of chest CT findings and oxygen saturation we tailored our therapy. As we had managed our patients at the university, we initiated remdesivir on admission, and began dexamethasone in those with an oxygen saturation below 94%. In the absence of a clear bacterial infection, we refrained from administering antibiotics. Unlike the surrounding hospitals, where antibiotics were prescribed for all patients, only 13 (16%) of our patients received antibiotic treatment.

Because the lungs of many of our patients demonstrated infiltrates indicating inflammatory fluid, we avoided intravenous fluids that had the potential to increase lung fluid and worsen oxygenation. Only the eight (9.6%) of our patients who showed evidence of dehydration received intravenous fluids.

We also avoided the poly-pharmacy being practiced by the other hospitals in the area, where the anti-malaria drug hydroxychloroquine, the anti-worm agent ivermectin, broad spectrum antibiotics, and multiple vitamins were administered to all patients. Patients at these other hospitals also all received IV fluids.

The average duration of stay in our hospital was 5.3 days, and only one patient died (1.2% mortality), the remaining patients being discharged to home. Our length-of-stay and exceptionally low mortality rate contrasted with the other hospitals in the area, where the average length-of-stay was nearly ten days, and the average mortality was 15%. Our hospital became the preferred destination for COVID-19 patients in our rural district.

I could not have been more pleased with our efforts, both at home and abroad. We had guided a superb team of Indian doctors who provided the most up-to-date and scientifically based care and had saved many lives. The Indian physicians acknowledged our expertise and embraced a standardized management plan. Using Zoom we huddled together like a group of worker bees and came to a consensus on how best to manage each patient.

The Successful Application of TPS for Mass Vaccination

During the COVID-19 pandemic, I also witnessed the remarkable benefits of applying a standardized approach to administering the SARS-CoV-2 vaccine.

By applying TPS principles, we maximized the efficiency of mass vaccination in our university community. By early April 2021, there were sufficient vaccine supplies to allow all individuals 16 years of age or older to be immunized with the Pfizer or Moderna mRNA vaccine. The president of the university assigned a health center team to immunize 52,000 students over 40 days, from early April to the end of the semester, in mid-May. Because everyone would require two shots spaced three weeks apart, this would require 104,000 total injections or an average of 2,600 vaccinations per day.

A 32,000-square-foot athletic booster hall was reserved as our mass vaccination site. We created eight vaccination sites: six with one workstation, and two at either end of the large hall with two workstations. Each station had five sites to visit (Figure 9-3). The distances between these sites were six feet (the shortest distance recommended to minimize person-to-person spread of the SARS-CoV-2 virus). These short distances minimized walk time.

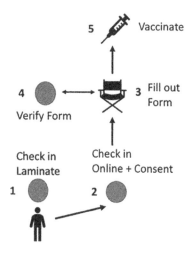

Figure 9-3. Physical layout of a single vaccine workstation.

The first workstation site was the pre-check-in table where the clerk filled out the laminated visual control sheet. The name and birth date of the person receiving the vaccine were entered, along with their arrival time. The sheet had checkboxes for computer cloud check-in, consent form signature, as well as the vaccine to be injected – 'P' for Pfizer and 'M' for Moderna– and the first or second dose. For example, if it was the first shot of the Pfizer vaccine, 'P1' would be entered. There were also boxes to enter the time of vaccine injection and time of discharge from observation.

This laminated sheet allowed each downstream person to assure that the previous site had completed their work, maximizing reliability. The times of check-in and vaccine injection were entered into a cloud server by the station runner, allowing the supervisor for the center to monitor the pace of vaccination at each workstation. If times exceeded ten minutes per person, someone from the central desk visited the workstation to identify the reasons for delay.

At the second site, the clerk checked off the person's name on the cloud website confirming their appointment (Figure 9-3). Next, the person being vaccinated traveled to the consent site, where a consent form was filled out (Site 3), and the person at that location confirmed that the consent form was properly filled out and signed (Site 4). The verifier then introduced the individual to one of the two health professionals responsible for administering the vaccine (Site 5). While cleaning the arm with alcohol and administering the mRNA vaccine, the vaccinator explained potential side effects. If someone had reported potential allergies on their consent form, after receiving the vaccine, they were asked to sit in the nearby waiting area for a 15-minute observation period.

By timing each of these steps for six different patients, the median time for each step was determined, and this time expectation was relayed as a time guideline for the individual responsible for each site. After creating these workflow expectations, we found that the average throughput (time from check-in to vaccination) dropped from 13 to 9 minutes per person.

By applying this workflow, each vaccinator was able to administer 25 shots per hour. Over ten hours, twenty vaccinators were expected to administer 5,000 vaccinations per day, and for five of the days we achieved this goal. On other days, demand did not rise to this level and the number of vaccinations varied from 649 (on weekend days) to 2,818 per day. Over the 40-day period, our mass vaccination site administered 35,453 vaccine doses and, compared to the reports from other mass vaccination sites, we achieved three-to-four-fold higher productivity. The county where we administered the vaccine contains 1.2% of the state's population. During the time period of our mass vaccination, we were responsible for 2.0% of all the vaccinations administered in the state. (39)

Given the high level of protection the vaccine provides, our mass vaccination center is likely to have saved many lives. I was particularly excited that a standardized process guided by the tools of TPS had dramatically improved the productivity of our vaccination center. We had created the perfect beehive.

Consider the benefits if this approach was applied throughout our healthcare delivery systems!

Chapter 10: Conclusions – Learning by Doing

Management of a system, therefore, requires knowledge of the interrelationships between all the components within the system. And of the people that work in it.
—W. Edward Deming

Being a cell biology investigator, I examined the systems of care within my university medical center by repeatedly applying the scientific method. The lessons I have learned are applicable not only to academic institutions but also to local hospitals whose sole mission is the care of patients.

How did our teams finally overcome resistance to change and implement life-saving changes to our systems of care? Successes were achieved by following the recommendations of experts in adaptive leadership and organizing people to bring about change. This chapter presents several key lessons about complex system change.

Lesson 1: Understand Micro-Systems

First, everyone working in health care must embrace the intricacy and complexity of the many micro-systems required to deliver care to patients. A helpful way to envision an individual health system is to think about the complex coordination within the beehive required to generate honey. Remember, without honey, the bee colony cannot survive. For honeybees, the effective coordination of work is truly a life-or-death challenge.

In the case of bees, it is likely this coordination is predominantly orchestrated by genetic codes that have been selected over millions of years to maximize the organization of work within the beehive (Figure 10-1). In the bee colony, each worker bee serves one of six roles to assure the smooth functioning of the hive.

The most important role is the forager, who flies to sites where nectar-containing flowers can be harvested. As part of their role, foragers are in constant communication with each other, sharing the locations of the richest supplies of nectar to assure the most efficient harvesting. A second role is to store the nectar. The forager bee regurgitates the nectar from its stomach to the receiver worker bee, who converts the nectar to honey and stores it in wax hexagonal honeycomb chambers. Other workers are assigned to guard the beehive entrance, clean the honeycombs, and groom both the queen and the drones.

Similarly, hospital personnel need to fully understand their roles and faithfully supply the services required to provide ideal patient care. Too often, roles are not completely defined or understood. Thorough descriptions of roles (or 'playbooks') for each member of the care team are critical for the smooth coordination of care.

Unfortunately, in health care, physical distances between different services can mean people do not appreciate the importance of coordinating care with other personnel. They don't, for example, witness the downstream and upstream effects of their behaviors. Health professionals, particularly physicians, too often prefer to work alone and assume they can improve the safety of patient care merely by trying harder. However, all experts in the field of quality and safety know that **trying harder is not the solution**. We all need to work together in highly effective and efficient systems.

Lesson 2: Develop Systems Thinking

Few physicians are systems thinkers. Instead, individual creativity has been emphasized and rewarded, and the standardized job descriptions and protocols required to create seamless interfaces between personnel and activities have been resisted. Yet, the human brain is naturally error-prone, and so human engineers have emphasized the importance of **standardization to reduce human error and achieve higher reliability.**

Imagine if a significant percentage of worker bees decided not to harvest nectar. The bee colony would run out of honey over the winter and die. Similarly, refusal to standardize work increases the risk of medical errors and the likelihood of preventable patient deaths. And unlike in bee colonies, evolution and genetic selection will not solve the challenge of achieving highly reliable coordinated health care.

To achieve effective coordination, healthcare professionals need to also **understand each customer-supplier relationship.** The physician and nurse should be continually supplying information to their patients about their illnesses and continually updating them about the rationale and time expectations of their management plans. Physicians should be supplying the bedside nurse with the daily plan for each patient, and the nurses should be updating the physician on each patient's present condition with regards to vital signs, symptoms, and psychological state.

We must embrace change in how we practice medicine, and this means we must embrace standardization. Healthcare systems must be converted from collections of independent personnel, divisions, and departments into coordinated beehives by applying the principles of the Toyota Production System (TPS).

Lesson 3: Alignment is Crucial

Another major challenge for all healthcare systems is for everyone to be aligned with the institution's primary goal.

The members of the beehive have one major goal: to produce honey. The worker bee's efforts are aligned to generate sufficient honey to survive the winter by harvesting nectar and pollen during the spring and summer. Honey supplies sufficient calories for heat generation by a bee's flight muscles during the cold winters, and fuels the twelve million miles foraging bees are required to fly in their search of nectar and pollen.

The alignment of their goals enables the coordination of 80,000 bees within a single beehive (Figure 10-1).

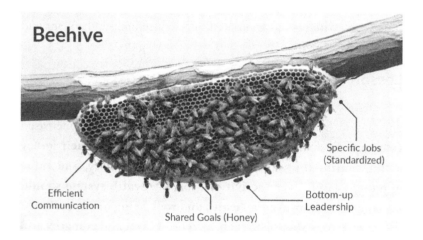

Figure 10-1. Key characteristics of the beehive system.

Many large healthcare systems have 20,000 to 30,000 employees, which is comparable to a single beehive. However, not only are the job descriptions (or playbooks) poorly understood, but the goals of the individuals within these systems are rarely aligned. What defines 'honey' varies from hive to hive, as well as from person to person. For many, honey is defined financially (e.g., how much revenue is each worker bee generating?). Many physicians are judged by the number of work units – Relative Value Units (RVUs) – they generate.

In most areas of the US, the prevailing reimbursement system is fee-for-service. Each test or procedure ordered generates a bill that must be paid by the health insurance company or the patient. The more procedures a physician performs, the higher the RVU's. The more tests and procedures performed, the higher the healthcare system's revenue. The danger of this definition of honey is that profits may be valued over patients.

Financial reward diminishes altruism and has the potential to encourage healthcare professionals to view patients as sources of income rather than sources of inspiration and compassion. When fee-for-service is the reimbursement system and the definition of honey is monetary, waste reduction and efforts to achieve high-value patient care are not rewarded. For example, the reduced lengths of stay for my patients has translated into reduced reimbursement and *lower* RVU values.

Lesson 4: Nectar (and Other Rewards)

Systems are designed to produce the outcomes they achieve, and our present healthcare system is rewarding overuse and increased volume. Therefore, healthcare systems should **define their honey as the continual improvement of the quality, safety, and value of patient care. Every activity within the health system should be *designed* to improve the health and well-being of our patients**. These activities should be seen as acts of love, and empathy and compassion should naturally follow.

A major challenge will be our present system of private healthcare insurers. These companies are profit-driven, and without major changes at the national level, healthcare delivery systems risk financial losses. For this reason, many organizations – including the Right Care Alliance (RCA) (see chapter 3 – 'Beginning Again') – are campaigning for universal health care that focuses on population health and value-based care. I encourage everyone concerned about our present healthcare system to **get involved in a grassroots community organization and fight for a more just, transparent, patient-centered healthcare system that values patients over profits**.

If you are thinking, "I don't have time, and my efforts won't make a difference anyway", remember the words of Rev. William Sloan Coffin: "If we don't make a difference by trying, we will make a difference by not trying."

Many small steps can add up to a large step. When it comes to the US healthcare system, it will take a grass roots revolution to overcome the many special interests with a stake in the status quo. The more people who join the revolution the greater their power to bring about change.

Lesson 5: Begin with the Workers

Another important characteristic of beehives is bottom-up leadership. All worker bees are equal in status and decisions about the locations for the harvesting of pollen and nectar, as well as the locations of new nests, are made by consensus. There are no supervisors, there is no hierarchy, and the system of leadership is distributive. Every worker bee is empowered to share their viewpoint, so that the beehive runs very much like a town hall (Figure 10-1).

As you've read, however, healthcare systems have a very different leadership structure. As discussed in chapter 8, these systems have multiple hierarchies, and eliminating the steep power gradients will be critical for future improvement.

An aspiration for all healthcare systems is to encourage a **distributive leadership model** as opposed to a top-down micromanagement system. **Humility and empathy are critical leadership characteristics** that should be encouraged when promoting a culture of patient safety. A disrespectful (toxic) culture makes improving patient care quality and safety nearly impossible. Arrogance and steep hierarchies are dangerous and should be addressed.

Lesson 6: Continually Adapt

So, to emulate honeybees, we need an increase in reliability, the alignment of goals (i.e., a single definition of honey), and a flattening of hierarchies. These changes represent profound adaptive changes. Personal experience has shown that the most effective way to bring about these changes will be to train adaptive leaders capable of applying the organizing practices of successful politicians to transform our healthcare systems.

Let's review a few key facts about **adaptive leadership** as they are described in chapter 6.

Leading change is difficult, because in most cases, those in power favor the status quo, and proposals for change can create a sense of loss and emotional stress, what Professor Ron Heifetz calls 'emotional disequilibrium'. Higher-level administrators must understand the importance of supporting adaptive leaders. When adaptive leaders are successful in changing the way things are done, they are often labeled as 'troublemakers'. Therefore, senior administrators and adaptive leaders seeking change must be patient and understanding and persevere. Additionally, adaptive leaders need protection, support and should be rewarded for the courage required to continue their work in the face of resistance.

The implementation of new discoveries has been slow in healthcare due to cumbersome hierarchies, and because many physicians and administrators belong to the 'late majority' or 'laggards' categories of Rogers' Diffusion of Innovations Theory (chapter 6 –What Beekeepers Know). In fact, the average lag period from discovery of a new treatment until adoption is 17 years!

The snail's pace at which new treatments and procedures are accepted remains a major impediment to improving patient safety. The hope is that deliberate adaptive leadership can accelerate these important changes.

Yet the management of excessive emotional disequilibrium may require *slowing* the speed of change. Moving too quickly leads, for example, to name-calling, just as moving too quickly when handling bees can result in bee stings. Beekeepers use smoke to calm bees, and adaptive leaders and senior administrators should employ empathetic listening and emphasize the benefits of change to reduce emotional disequilibrium.

The leadership at my institution did not understand adaptive leadership and I did not effectively communicate my goals during my early system-wide efforts. Close alignment and continual communication are critical, particularly in the early stages of adaptive change. These conditions were eventually achieved in the Hospital Medicine Division, accounting for our many successful improvements.

Because meaningful and sustainable change must come from the bottom up and not from the top down, adaptive leaders should not have high-level administrative positions that involve significant power over those they are encouraging to change. **Adaptive leaders should not have power over but rather have power with** those trying to bring about change.

Adaptive leaders should **never work alone**. Instead, they can recruit others to help them lead change. Over time the effective adaptive leader identifies new champions, trains them to become effective adaptive leaders, and then steps back to become a coach and adviser. In this way, one adaptive leader can impact multiple change initiatives in multiple divisions and departments.

As an adaptive leader, one must assess the willingness of each individual to embrace change and **focus primarily on the 'early adopters' and the 'early majority'**. If the adaptive leader can persuade these two groups, the late majority will soon follow. **Beware of laggards** because they usually cannot be persuaded. A laggard in a position of power can block change and delay progress (as happened with the AIR project – see chapter 4 – 'Field Conditions').

The ability to persuade and to create camaraderie and trust requires the same organizing skills used by nearly all successful politicians and public figures. Martin Luther King Jr., for example, recruited huge numbers of people to his causes by applying the fundamentals of effective organizing. Using these same methods for the past decade, I have become increasingly effective at recruiting fellow faculty and other hospital personnel to make significant changes in how we care for patients.

Lesson 7: Leverage Strengths

Appreciative Inquiry is an important approach that can reduce the emotional stress of change by emphasizing the positives – rather than negatives – in the present condition and building on them. Appreciative Inquiry also encourages those on the front lines to create solutions, assuring that change comes from the bottom up, rather than being mandated from above.

Organizing skill 1: Effective one-on-one meetings

As described in the preceding chapters, the first and most important skill is to conduct effective **one-on-one meetings**. Nelson Mandela, the first post-apartheid President of South Africa, provides a dramatic example of the power of one-on-one meetings. He was confined to jail for 27 years. Rather than becoming bitter and withdrawn, he constantly met with fellow political prisoners and shared his vision for multi-racial governance. (40)

Few people achieve the stature of Nelson Mandela, but we can all become effective one-on-one campaigners. Those who care for patients have already been taught and practice effective one-on-one interactions, and these skills are fundamental for creating the ideal patient-healthcare professional relationship. In all effective interpersonal relationships, each person must be willing to share something that the other person values. By showing genuine interest in others, I was able to forge life-long relationships and join with others to begin to transform our local health system.

One-on-one interactions must always be honest and forthright, and from the very start it is important to inform an individual when recruiting them to join a campaign. For instance, I asked each person to join me for coffee to explore how we could work together to promote the 'I Promise' campaign. These one-on-one meetings were invigorating and enjoyable because sharing stories with others is a fundamental human activity; by nature, we are very social animals.

The meetings not only laid the foundation for the campaign but also improved interpersonal connections.

Organizing skill 2: Personal narrative

The second important organizing skill is perfecting the **personal narrative**. Throughout my campaigns to improve the quality and safety of patient care, I have shared the story of Mary's near-death, which elicits strong emotions in the listener. Neurobiologists have found that one of the key regions of the brain responsible for emotions is the amygdala, and this structure is extensively connected to the prefrontal cortex, the region of the brain just beneath the forehead that is responsible for decision-making. (19)

The result, as experienced politicians know, is that emotions can lead to changes in opinion. Emotions can alter decision-making and motivate action. Effective personal narrative arouses feelings and encourages the audience to act. Three components of personal narrative should be combined to motivate goal-directed commitment: a 'Story of Self', a 'Story of Us', and a 'Story of Now'. In most effective narratives the Story of Self leads seamlessly into the Story of Us and is followed by the Story of Now (see chapter 6 –'Organizing for Change').

As mentioned earlier, one of the most effective practitioners of personal narrative was Martin Luther King Jr. He described his personal fears and the suffering so many experienced simply because of the color of their skin. His lyrical dialogue and soaring voice generated deep emotions and empathy. Even today, his 'I Have a Dream' speech brings tears to my eyes (and I'm sure that I'm not alone in this).

A well-crafted personal narrative has a far greater likelihood of motivating healthcare providers than sending email requests, creating a web-based educational program, giving a dry informational lecture, or placing posters on doors. The creation of a personal narrative is an iterative process and will change over time, depending on the audience, prevailing attitude, and current conditions. The speaker should avoid a fixed script and allow the narrative to evolve and improve over time, as one becomes a more skilled and perceptive narrator.

Organizing skill 3: Effective meetings

The third important organizing tool is bringing potential recruits together in **larger public meetings**.

Some politicians use large rallies, and these can also be used in health care to encourage system-wide changes. Other large gatherings can be effective for sharing new ideas and suggestions for improvement, including weekly grand rounds and monthly or bimonthly division and department business meetings. These are ideal venues for introducing new ideas and new quality improvement approaches in a non-threatening forum. In times of crisis (such as the COVID-19 pandemic), weekly town hall meetings are the ideal forum for sharing ideas and designing solutions to unexpected challenges.

Meeting speakers should emphasize innovation and describe the potential advantages to the audience. For example, when discussing the implementation of Athletic-based Interprofessional Rounds (AIR), I emphasized to both faculty and residents the time saved and the ability to complete patient care tasks more efficiently. Whenever possible, presentations should begin with a personal narrative.

When introducing the bedside checklist, I begin with story of an 18-month-old child treated for second-degree and third-degree burns after falling into a bathtub filled with scalding hot water. The patient was steadily improving and was transferred from the Pediatric Intensive Care Unit (PICU) to the regular floor. Prior to transfer, her central intravenous line was discontinued; however, she was kept 'NPO', meaning she was not allowed to take anything by mouth. Over the next 48 hours, she became increasingly dehydrated. When given a narcotic pain medication, she developed shock resulting in irreversible brain damage and death.

If the team had conducted bedside rounds with the nurse using the TEMP checklist (see chapter 8 – 'Plan: Building on Strengths'), they would have discussed 'T' for tubes and immediately realized that she had no intravenous line. Similarly, when discussing 'E', they would have understood that she was not eating and not taking anything by mouth. Based on the TEMP checklist, the team would have realized that she had received no fluids for 48 hours. They would have immediately initiated aggressive rehydration with oral and intravenous fluids and her tragic death would have been prevented. (41)

This personal story emphasizes how effective and efficient communication can save lives. The honeybee colony has incorporated this same skill through the waggle dance that can relay the location of a rich nectar source or ideal nest location within seconds.

When I tell this story, I address the elephant in the room: physician resistance to standardization. Standard protocols are derogatorily termed 'cookie-cutter medicine'. In response, I emphasize the fact that the human brain is error-prone and that when there are no standard operating protocols, physicians are required to use slow thinking for each care process. This increases their cognitive load, which in turn increases mental fatigue and the risk of cognitive error. Finally, I emphasize that when trying to improve the quality of care, it is impossible to improve a *random* process. A preliminary standard protocol serves as the first stage for improvement and allows the application of participative, plan-do-study-adjust cycles to make each process more efficient and effective over time.

Organizing skill 4: Effective strategies and tactics

The fourth and final skill required for organizing is the creation of effective **strategies and tactics.**

This is a unique skill that is rarely taught in college or medical school. Once a leadership team is recruited through one-on-one meetings, the first task is to decide on the goal of the project and what measurement tools will be used to monitor campaign progress.

An important element of the strategy is **deciding on the reach of your campaign**. For example, our 'I Promise' campaign encompassed the entire hospital, and my initial AIR initiative was implemented within the Department of Medicine. The preliminary tactic or tool was to hold a **health system-sponsored forum** on doctor-patient communication. As described in chapter 7, two patients – one of whom was a physician – shared their stories of self. Patients, nurses, administrators, and physicians in the audience raised their hands immediately following these personal stories. Everyone's input was valued, and all were brimming with unique ideas on how to improve communication. Experience suggests that campaigns are more likely to have impact if confined to a single division with 50–100 employees rather than departments with up to 1,000 employees.

Another tactic that I have found helpful is the creation of **web pages** that clearly outline the components of each standardized protocol. Web pages can be continually updated as the protocols are adjusted, and the sites can be made accessible to all caregivers and patients.

Short instructional videos (i.e., less than ten minutes long), which clearly describe new protocols and their rationale to enhance implementation, are also helpful. Thanks to virtual communication tools like Zoom, anyone with a laptop computer can now record instructional videos.

As discussed in chapter 8, another necessary tactic that is often overlooked is **continual monitoring** of the improvement project. Ideally, students with score sheets can observe how accurately the team members are conducting the standardized protocol. If a protocol is not being faithfully adhered to, there will be no improvement. We found that effective and **meaningful improvement is achieved when adherence exceeds 70%.** Finally, the observers should share their scores with those implementing the improvement to provide **actionable feedback**.

The Ideal Healthcare Delivery System

Finally, after adopting these lessons what should the ideal healthcare delivery system look like?

Let me share my front-line perspective. As shown in Figure 10-2, the system should have a single goal; a single definition of honey – patient-centered care and improving the health and well-being of patients. Academic medical centers almost always include this goal, but add multiple other goals, diluting the importance of focusing on the patient. When a faculty member or other healthcare professional is working in the patient care arena, they should be encouraged to continually look through the eyes of their patients. Experts in TPS maintain that when there is a relentless focus on what the customer desires, financial reward naturally follows.

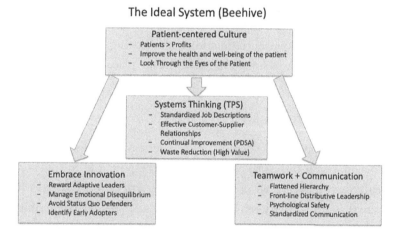

Figure 10-2. Components of the Ideal Healthcare Delivery System. TPS, Toyota Production System. PDSA, Plan–Do–Study–Adjust.

I recommend that academic medical centers create a separate set of goals for biomedical research and education, rather than mixing the goals of the three missions together. A significant percentage of faculty will practice in all three arenas; however, when they are caring for patients, the focus should be on the patient. Focusing on other missions during patient care activity should be minimized through system redesigns and positive reminders. Remember the disastrous consequences when the senior physician was multi-tasking while caring for Mary (chapter 1 – 'Mary's Story').

For honeybees, a total focus on the acquisition of honey is genetically programmed. But, when it comes to humans, behavior change is primarily driven by reward, and healthcare professionals working in this arena should be rewarded for excellence in patient care. This requires a new set of reward criteria. In addition to patient volume, the safety, efficiency, and effectiveness of patient care needs to be measured and rewarded. With the developments of Artificial Intelligence (AI), machine learning can be applied to electronic medical records to generate more granular and accurate assessments of the quality of care. High patient satisfaction scores should also be considered when evaluating performance.

Based on my experience, in addition to having a patient-focused culture, three key elements need to be in place to achieve ideal patient care (Figure 10-2).

Systems approach

First and foremost, everyone must understand and embrace a systems approach to health care. TPS has the potential to transform healthcare delivery, but only if everyone participates. Experts estimate that productivity can be increased by up to 4-fold, while simultaneously reducing errors by 99%. (42) Embracing standardized job descriptions to assure integration of effort is critical, and those who can achieve 70% or higher adherence to each standard should be rewarded. In a fully integrated system, every member must understand each customer-supplier relationship and know what, where and when a service should be supplied.

The creativity and insights of those working on the front lines need to be captured by empowering everyone to make suggestions for improvement, and to continually apply plan-do-study-adjust cycles to implement these potentially beneficial changes. Finally, waste reduction should be ongoing during all activities. Healthcare professionals, patients and their families should continually ask, "Is this of value to the patient? Does this activity improve their health and well-being?"

Continual innovation

Second is the need to embrace continual innovation. This activity is a natural off shoot of TPS. In health care, the personal price of bringing about change can be high and, as discussed above, adaptive leaders need to be recognized, supported, and rewarded. One of the primary lessons I have learned in my leadership journey is how to manage emotional disequilibrium, and this needs to be a key strategic goal when managing change.

An undervalued personal trait that should be consciously selected for is a willingness to try new ways of doing things. Innovative organizations should be recruiting, rewarding, and advancing 'early adopters'. At the opposite end of the innovation spectrum is the laggard. The potential harm of those who resist change has rarely been discussed in health care, because too often it is those who 'don't make waves' who rise to the top of the leadership structure and assure maintenance of the status quo.

My personal experiences with medical errors, as well as those of others as described in chapter 3, combined with the fact that the healthcare industry has failed to reduce inpatient medical errors over the past two decades, (43) make it clear that there is an urgent need to embrace innovation.

Teamwork

The final key element is teamwork.

When teamwork is effective, morale and job satisfaction are high, and turnover can be dramatically reduced. Also, when the patient and family are included as part of the team, patient satisfaction can be markedly improved.

First and foremost, hierarchies need to be eliminated and individual expertise at all levels appreciated – including insights from patients and their families (remember the fatal case of prolonged QT syndrome, chapter 3 – Missed Diagnosis). This is a core condition for becoming a highly reliable organization, as well as for becoming a high-performing team. As emphasized by TPS, all participants should be encouraged to lead. Most decisions need to be made on the front lines by those doing the work, not made in distant offices.

To achieve this, psychological safety is a must. Respect and mutual appreciation create a sense of worth and encourage all employees to share their ideas and lead changes in their sphere of influence. When individuals feel socially connected, creativity thrives. A sense of belonging greatly enhances a sense of well-being and guards against burnout. (44) Finally, seamless communication is critical for teams to be effective, and the use of standardized communication tools assures that no details are missed, and that information is transmitted efficiently.

Achieving the Ideal Healthcare Delivery System

Are the ambitious goals set forth by honeybees impossible for humans to achieve?

Examples from aircraft carrier teams and forest fire fighters, (38) as well as my experiences described in this book, are proof that we can emulate honeybee colonies.

Earlier in my career, I envisioned teamwork as a process of harnessing the collective intelligence of each team member to cross-check all actions as the primary strategy for enhancing reliability. Everyone on the team would have each other's back. However, the risk of cognitive error remains a concern and, ideally, all clinical activity should be continually checked by computers, as is already done in the airline industry. When it comes to fatal crashes commercial airline flights have achieved a reliability of 0.16/million in 2022 (45) (below Six Sigma – 3.4 errors per million) because airline pilots now primarily play a supervisory role monitoring the minute-by-minute application of automatic computer algorithms.

In medicine, AI promises to be a key tool for navigating complex algorithms that can guide customized, up-to-date care. As with all adaptive change, health systems have been slow to adopt AI, and adaptive leadership and organizing methods will be required to accelerate its adoption. AI has the potential to improve the continuity of care, clinical decision making, quality and safety of care, value-based care, and clinical operations such as operating room utilization and ED-to-hospital patient flow. It can also guide systems improvement and the integration of care by medical teams. At present, the benefits of AI have yet to be realized in these areas, currently having only reached the pilot phase. (46)

I recently discovered the power of AI for improving the accuracy of diagnosis. Using the smart phone app 'Ask AI' (Codeway. com, Istanbul, Turkey), I asked the app: "What is the differential diagnosis for a 33-year-old female with a peripheral nerve injury of her leg, and 7,000 eosinophils/ml who had recently been taking amoxicillin."

The first diagnosis listed was a "drug reaction to amoxicillin." and the recommended management was to "discontinue amoxicillin and begin corticosteroids." If this app had been available in 1988, Mary would have received corticosteroid therapy on hospital admission and would not have suffered the many complications of her nearly fatal progressive allergic vasculitis.

I also asked the AI app, "What diseases could cause a teenage girl to suddenly lose consciousness and turn blue after being startled." (see chapter 3 – 'Missed Diagnosis') One of the leading diagnoses was a "cardiac arrhythmia such as long QT syndrome."

For medical educators, the implementation of the changes I have recommended will require a redesign of the curriculum for physicians, physician assistants, nurse practitioners and nurses, as well as those training in healthcare administration. All students will need to be introduced to the basics of AI. Memorizing of facts ('rote learning') should be deemphasized, because with the advent of AI as well as powerful search engines, facts are instantaneously accessible. Instead, training should focus on critical thinking; differential diagnosis; embracing and leading change; effective teamwork; as well as empathic, accurate, and efficient communication.

As the American Medical Association (AMA) now recommends, curricula also need to include health systems science; the third pillar of medical education after basic biomedical science and clinical medicine. (47)

Patients and the lay public are experiencing unrelenting rises in health care costs. Premiums for health insurance are consuming ever higher percentages of the family income, and deductibles and copayments of thousands of dollars are now common. The consequence: 4 out of 10 Americans have significant medical debts (over $250) and medical debt is the leading cause of bankruptcy in the US (48) As described earlier, fee-for-service is one of the major drivers of wasteful diagnostic tests and treatments. Another major driver is local healthcare system monopolies that continually raise fees. Adding to costs, many for-profit health insurance companies siphon 20–25% of healthcare premiums for administrative overheads. To make conditions even worse, as previously discussed, pharmaceutical companies are charging exorbitant prices for life-saving medications like insulin.

As recently stated in an insightful viewpoint in the *Journal of the American Medical Association*, the US health system is currently "driven by greed." (49)

Only a grass roots movement (Lesson 4) applying effective organizing methods (Lesson 7) has the potential to counter these forces. Healthcare professionals and citizens who understand what is at stake must work together. My hope is that readers of this book will join nonprofit health care reform organizations and get involved. Your voice combined with many others can make a difference, as we saw when protests from the lay public and healthcare professionals resulted in the cost of insulin being capped at $35/month.

Based on my many years on the front lines of healthcare quality improvement, I firmly believe that it is possible to achieve the goals first outlined in 2000 by the seminal call-to-action report by the Institute of Medicine, 'To Err is Human'. (50) This can be done by focusing on a single shared goal, universally adopting TPS, embracing continual innovation, and practicing effective teamwork supported by AI machine learning.

These experts envisioned the transformation of healthcare delivery systems to fulfill the ideal conditions summarized by the mnemonic STEEEP. Our future health systems promise to be safe, timely, efficient, effective, equitable and patient centered.

Final Thoughts

To create an integrated healthcare delivery system analogous to a beehive requires the careful management of human behavior. We will all need to become effective beekeepers who move slowly and with sensitivity. To avoid excessive resistance or bee stings, we will need to use soothing smoke in the form of empathetic listening and continual dialogue to calm those who react negatively to change.

When applying the approaches presented in this book – Appreciative Inquiry, the beehive model, and TPS – be alert to the potential dangers of emotional disequilibrium. Those of us who want to see change in health care must become comfortable playing with the bees and harvesting honey from one beehive at a time.

References

1. Southwick F. Who was caring for Mary? Ann Intern Med. 1993;118(2):146-8.

2. Seeley TD. Honeybee democracy. Princeton: Princeton University Press; 2010. 273 p.

3. Seeley TD. The lives of bees : the untold story of the honey bee in the wild. Princeton, NJ: Princeton University Press; 2019. xiii, 353 p.

4. Buchmann S. What a bee knows : exploring the thoughts, memories, and personalities of bees. Washington: Island Press; 2023. 296 p.

5. Southwick FS. I Lost My Leg to a Medical Error. New York Times 2013.

6. Boothman RC, Imhoff SJ, Campbell DA, Jr. Nurturing a culture of patient safety and achieving lower malpractice risk through disclosure: lessons learned and future directions. Front Health Serv Manage. 2012;28(3):13-28.

7. Southwick FS, Cranley NM, Hallisy JA. A patient-initiated voluntary online survey of adverse medical events: the perspective of 696 injured patients and families. BMJ Qual Saf. 2015;24(10):620-9.

8. Elrod JM, Karnad AB. Boston City Hospital and the Thorndike Memorial Laboratory: the birth of modern haematology. Br J Haematol. 2003;121(3):383-9.

9. Finland M. Treatment of pneumonia and other serious infections. N Engl J Med. 1960;263:207-21.

10. Kazanjian PH. Efforts to regulate antibiotic misuse in hospitals: A history. Infect Control Hosp Epidemiol. 2022;43(9):1119-22.

11. Canadian Critical Care Trials G. A randomized trial of diagnostic techniques for ventilator-associated pneumonia. N Engl J Med. 2006;355(25):2619-30.

12. Berton DC, Kalil AC, Teixeira PJ. Quantitative versus qualitative cultures of respiratory secretions for clinical outcomes in patients

with ventilator-associated pneumonia. Cochrane Database Syst Rev. 2014(10):CD006482.

13. Fernando SM, Tran A, Cheng W, Klompas M, Kyeremanteng K, Mehta S, et al. Diagnosis of ventilator-associated pneumonia in critically ill adult patients-a systematic review and meta-analysis. Intensive Care Med. 2020;46(6):1170-9.

14. Spear SJ. Learning to lead at Toyota. Harv Bus Rev. 2004;82(5):78-86, 151.

15. Southwick FS, Spear SJ. Commentary: "Who was caring for Mary?" revisited: a call for all academic physicians caring for patients to focus on systems and quality improvement. Acad Med. 2009;84(12):1648-50.

16. Southwick FS. Critically ill : a five-point plan to cure healthcare delivery. Carlsbad, CA: No Limit Pub. Group; 2012. 360 p

17. The Auto Lemon Index: Which top-selling auto manufacturers are sued the most, and the least, over defective cars in California? [Internet]. 1922. Available from: https://publicinterestnetwork.org/wp-content/uploads/2022/05/Auto-Lemon-Index-CAP-CARS-FG-May22.pdf.

18. Bharwani AM, Harris GC, Southwick FS. Perspective: a business school view of medical interprofessional rounds: transforming rounding groups into rounding teams. Acad Med. 2012;87(12):1768-71.

19. Heifetz RA, Grashow A, Linsky M. The practice of adaptive leadership : tools and tactics for changing your organization and the world. Boston, Mass.: Harvard Business Press; 2009. xvi, 326 p.

20. Chang WW, Wu MT, Chang YC, Hu WY. The mediating effect of shared decision-making in enhancing patient satisfaction with participation in cancer clinical trials. Asia Pac J Oncol Nurs. 2023;10(8):100265.

21. Shay LA, Lafata JE. Where is the evidence? A systematic review of shared decision making and patient outcomes. Med Decis Making. 2015;35(1):114-31.

22. Rogers EM. Diffusion of innovations. 5th ed. New York: Free Press;

2003. xxi, 551 p.

23. Southwick F, Lewis M, Treloar D, Cherabuddi K, Radhakrishnan N, Leverence R, et al. Applying athletic principles to medical rounds to improve teaching and patient care. Acad Med. 2014;89(7):1018-23.

24. Archibald LK, Shapiro J, Pass A, Rand K, Southwick F. Methicillin-resistant Staphylococcus aureus infection in a college football team: risk factors outside the locker room and playing field. Infect Control Hosp Epidemiol. 2008;29(5):450-3.

25. Merriel A, Wilson A, Decker E, Hussein J, Larkin M, Barnard K, et al. Systematic review and narrative synthesis of the impact of Appreciative Inquiry in health care. BMJ Open Qual. 2022;11(2).

26. Gravina N, Sleiman A, Southwick FS, Matey N, Harlan E, Lukose K, et al. Increasing adherence to a standardized rounding procedure in two hospital in-patient units. J Appl Behav Anal. 2021;54(4):1514-25.

27. Radhakrishnan NS, Lukose K, Cartwright R, Sleiman A, Matey N, Lim D, et al. Prospective application of the interdisciplinary bedside rounding checklist 'TEMP' is associated with reduced infections and length of hospital stay. BMJ Open Qual. 2022;11(4).

28. Vijayanand P, Wilkins E, Woodhead M. Severe acute respiratory syndrome (SARS): a review. Clin Med (Lond). 2004;4(2):152-60.

29. Kiang MV, Carlasare LE, Thadaney Israni S, Norcini JJ, Zaman JAB, Bibbins-Domingo K. Excess Mortality Among US Physicians During the COVID-19 Pandemic. JAMA Intern Med. 2023;183(4):374-6.

30. Mitja O, Corbacho-Monne M, Ubals M, Alemany A, Suner C, Tebe C, et al. A Cluster-Randomized Trial of Hydroxychloroquine for Prevention of Covid-19. N Engl J Med. 2021;384(5):417-27.

31. Group RC, Horby P, Mafham M, Linsell L, Bell JL, Staplin N, et al. Effect of Hydroxychloroquine in Hospitalized Patients with Covid-19. N Engl J Med. 2020;383(21):2030-40.

32. Bhaskar ME, Arun S. SARS-CoV-2 Infection Among Community Health Workers in India Before and After Use of Face Shields. JAMA. 2020;324(13):1348-9.

33. Chu DK, Akl EA, Duda S, Solo K, Yaacoub S, Schunemann HJ, et al. Physical distancing, face masks, and eye protection to prevent person-to-person transmission of SARS-CoV-2 and COVID-19: a systematic review and meta-analysis. Lancet. 2020;395(10242):1973-

87.

34. Adenaiye OO, Lai J, Bueno de Mesquita PJ, Hong F, Youssefi S, German J, et al. Infectious Severe Acute Respiratory Syndrome Coronavirus 2 (SARS-CoV-2) in Exhaled Aerosols and Efficacy of Masks During Early Mild Infection. Clin Infect Dis. 2022;75(1):e241-e8.

35. Landry SA, Subedi D, Barr JJ, MacDonald MI, Dix S, Kutey DM, et al. Fit-Tested N95 Masks Combined With Portable High-Efficiency Particulate Air Filtration Can Protect Against High Aerosolized Viral Loads Over Prolonged Periods at Close Range. J Infect Dis. 2022;226(2):199-207.

36. Recovery Collaborativer Group, Horby P, Lim WS, Emberson JR, Mafham M, Bell JL, et al. Dexamethasone in Hospitalized Patients with Covid-19. N Engl J Med. 2021;384(8):693-704.

37. Beigel JH, Tomashek KM, Dodd LE, Mehta AK, Zingman BS, Kalil AC, et al. Remdesivir for the Treatment of Covid-19 - Final Report. N Engl J Med. 2020;383(19):1813-26.

38. Weick KE, Sutcliffe KM. Managing the unexpected : sustained performance in a complex world. Third edition. ed. Hoboken, New Jersey: Wiley; 2015. xi, 209 p.

39. Froman MN, Walser MP, Lauzardo M, Graban M, Southwick FS. Applying Lean principles to create a high throughput mass COVID-19 vaccination site. BMJ Open Qual. 2022;11(1).

40. Mandela N. Long walk to freedom : the autobiography of Nelson Mandela. 1st ed. Boston: Little, Brown and Company; 1994. 656 p.

41. King S. Josie's story. 1st ed. New York: Atlantic Monthly Press; 2009. 275 p.

42. Koenigsaecker G. Leading the Lean Engerprise Transformation. Boca Raton, FL: CRC Press; 2013. 242 p.

43. Bates DW, Levine DM, Salmasian H, Syrowatka A, Shahian DM, Lipsitz S, et al. The Safety of Inpatient Health Care. N Engl J Med. 2023;388(2):142-53.

44. Southwick SM, Southwick FS. The Loss of Social Connectedness as a Major Contributor to Physician Burnout: Applying Organizational and Teamwork Principles for Prevention and Recovery. JAMA Psychiatry. 2020;77(5):449-50.

45. International Air Transportation Association Safety Report [Internet]. 2022. Available from: https://www.iata.org/en/publications/

safety-report/.

46. Graban M, Ebl. Lean hospitals : improving quality, patient safety, and employee engagement: Taylor and Francis; 2008.

47. Maben-Feaster R, Hammoud, M.M., Borkan, J., DeWaters, A., Gonzalo, J.D. and Starr, S.R. Health Systems Science Education. Philadelphia, PA: Elsevier; 2022. 180 p.

48. Levey, N.N. 100 Million people in America are saddled with health-care debt.. Kaiser Health News 2022.

49. Berwick DM. Salve Lucrum: The Existential Threat of Greed in US Health Care. JAMA. 2023;329(8):629-30.

50. Kohn LT, Corrigan J, Donaldson MS. To err is human : building a safer health system. Washington, D.C.: National Academy Press; 2000. xxi, 287 p.

About the Author

Dr. Frederick Southwick is a graduate of Yale College and the Columbia College of Physicians and Surgeons. He trained in internal medicine at Boston City Hospital and in infectious diseases at the Massachusetts General Hospital. He is a tenured professor of medicine and served as the Chief of Infectious Diseases at a major university medical center for 19 years. He was an active NIH funded biomedical investigator for thirty years, studying how bacteria interact with the human host, and has published more than 100 peer-reviewed research papers.

Dr. Southwick is presently the Director of Patient Care Quality and Safety for an academic Division of Hospital Medicine, applying the principles of Toyota Production System to improve patient care. He is also the creator of three Coursera massive open online courses: 'Fixing Healthcare Delivery' (30,000 students), 'Fixing Healthcare Delivery 2.0: Advanced Lean' (4,500 students), and 'COVID-19: A Clinical Update' (over 20,000 students).

He is an active member of the Right Care Alliance (RCA), a nonprofit organization dedicated to reforming health care to make the US system affordable, effective, safe, and accessible to all. Continuing his interest in competitive sports that began with playing on high school and college varsity athletic teams he now competes in master's rowing and marathon canoeing.

Also by Frederick S. Southwick, MD

Infectious Diseases: A clinical short course
McGraw-Hill Lange Series May 2020

This comprehensive textbook summarize the key points about all the major infectious diseasesand is designed to be read in 30 days. The tables and illustrations summarize detailed content. Guiding questions begin each chapter. A summary of key points are included in text boxes throughout the book. On completing this book you will have a deep understanding of infectious diserases.

Critically Ill: A 5-point Plan to Cure Healthcare Delivery No Limits Press, June 2012

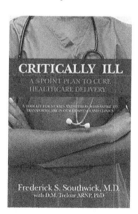

Dr. Southwick shares his concerns about the high number of annual preventable deaths due to medical errors in the U.S. and throughout the world. As a practicing clinician, investigator and scholar he devoted a year to deeply investigate the challenges we face to transform our health system. He provides a blue print for achieving the changes our health system so badly needs.

Made in the USA
Las Vegas, NV
06 July 2024

91969574R00095